UPON ARRIVAL

A Fictionalized Memoir in Diary Form

Told In the Seasons of the Year.

MILES CIGOLLE

SUNSTONE
PRESS

SANTA FE

Sunstone books may be purchased for educational, business, or sales promotional use. For information please write: Special Markets Department, Sunstone Press, P.O. Box 2321, Santa Fe, New Mexico 87504-2321.
Printed on acid-free paper
∞
eBook: 978-1-61139-753-6

———————————

Library of Congress Cataloging-in-Publication Data

Names: Cigolle, Miles author
Title: Upon arrival : a fictionalized memoir in diary form told in the seasons of the year / Miles Cigolle.
Description: Santa Fe, New Mexico : Sunstone Press, 2025. | Summary: "In his darkest moments the author was blessed with love for himself and his brothers, all detailed in this frank diary"-- Provided by publisher.
Identifiers: LCCN 2025026710 | ISBN 9781632936868 paperback | ISBN 9781611397536 epub
Subjects: LCSH: Cigolle, Miles--Fiction | Gay men--New York (State)--New York--History--20th century--Fiction. | West Village (New York, N.Y.)--History--20th century--Fiction | LCGFT: Autobiographical fiction | Gay fiction | Novels
Classification: LCC PS3603.I354 U66 2025 | DDC 813/.6--dc23/eng/20250610
LC record available at https://lccn.loc.gov/2025026710

———————————

WWW.SUNSTONEPRESS.COM
SUNSTONE PRESS / POST OFFICE BOX 2321 / SANTA FE, NM 87504-2321 /USA
(505) 988-4418

PREFACE

Join Miles and his new gay family in Upon Arrival, a fictionalized memoir based largely on real events and real people covering the year 1982 in New York City.

After a sexually-charged solo trip to Venice in the dead of winter, Miles's nine-year-old, picture-perfect, monogamous relationship with the college professor Jim falls apart, thrusting Miles into the tumultuous gay party years following Stonewall. AIDS is a distant rumble. Join Miles on his journey through the backrooms and sex clubs, the bath houses and tearooms of the West Village. Follow the candid daily entries in Miles's diary as he searches high and low for his new beloved Abbey. Thank God he finds his therapist Terrence along the way. Upon Arrival celebrates one gay man's eventual triumph over loneliness and despair. It's the tale of maturation, genuine friendship and true love.

1

WINTER

FRIDAY JANUARY 1, 1982

It's early winter in a new year, 1982. This will be my first diary. We'll see how it goes. I'm skeptical. My lover Jim thinks it's a good idea. I wonder why? Maybe he thinks I need some introspection. He'd be right about that. I'm a mess. He gave me the diary as a Christmas present. Its black leather cover looks like a Bible. It's embossed in gold letters "My Diary." A bit much, don't you think? He chose the model without the locking clasp. I guess he thinks we don't have any secrets. Dead wrong. I'd have chosen the model with the lock. Anyway, the lock is pretty meaningless, it's just for show. Maybe I'll enjoy writing a diary. All my secrets, right? Raunchy sex. Isn't sex the main thing people write about in their diary?

I turned thirty last October. I feel awkward for my age. I'm practically a middle-aged gay man and I've hardly experienced anything around sex in the real world. After Cornell and Ithaca, Jim and I lived together in Brooklyn Heights for over three years. Then we moved to Manhattan two years ago, into an artist's loft near City Hall. That part of my life is great. I mean, the part about living in an artist's loft in Manhattan, that's terrific. The rest is pathetic.

My sex life is awfully limited. Before I met Jim I had maybe three or four one-night stands with guys from Morrie's, the only gay bar in Ithaca; that's about it. They were all pretty awful, one gave me gonorrhea with a humiliating trip to Cornell Student Health Services. The exception was Johnny, the hippie flower child who lived downstairs. Johnny was my initiation into the world of gay sex. One night only, non-stop great sex all night long. He was a real sex guru. But unfortunately, Johnny wasn't available. He already had a "groovy" hippie lover. But he showed me how incredible gay sex could be. Johnny was terrific.

Anyhow, for a gay guy who's lived in New York City for six years it's pretty pathetic. Jim and I have been together for nine years in a closed monogamous relationship. The sex is okay, but it's predictable. Once a week I get to butt-fuck Jim on the bed or if I'm lucky on a rug in the living room. Sure, I can get into it, but I dream of a lot more. I fool around in gym steam rooms with strangers, but that's about it. No outside relationships. Plus, Jim's so uptight when it comes to sex. We never talk about it. He's like Terry my mother. God forbid if Jim would say something a little dirty that might turn me on like: "Hey Miles, let me suck you off while you're wearing your bomber jacket." That could never happen with Jim. He's too genteel, too Ivy League Princeton. It's a shame, I always crave a little raunchy sex.

I guess that's enough for my first day's entry. That wasn't so hard.

Saturday January 2, 1982

I joined a new gym today, sort of an informal New Year's resolution. The Apple Gym on Fulton Street. It's only two blocks from our loft. Jim declined. He hates gyms. I actually like gyms, the masculine atmosphere— the cute guys in the showers. And I could really use some muscles. I look like a damn sissy. If I set up a regular routine every weeknight after dinner for an hour or two, maybe I could get a few muscles.

The Apple Gym manager tells me it's almost always empty in the evenings. It's busiest during the lunch hour, catering to the Wall Street crowd. It's pretty basic, nothing fancy. The place is always hot and humid and it stinks of sweat. But it's really close to the loft, so I will probably use it.

Sunday January 3, 1982

My first real gym workout at Apple. The trainer was supposed to give me an introduction, walk me through the circuit of Nautilus machines, review the settings and the amount of weight for each. The usual gym stuff, but I wasn't expecting this Adonis. I could barely follow his instructions; I was more interested in what's inside his gym shorts than the correct setting on the bench press. Plus he really didn't make it easy. He was always smiling, leaning over me, adjusting my body position, touching my skin. The most intense exchange was on the chest press where he spotted me, his short muscular legs straddling my head as I lay on the bench looking up at the ceiling. He practically had his cock and balls in my mouth. I only wish right? His name was Adam, that's appropriate. God's first creation of man, perfect. He always gives me a warm hello. I can't tell if he's straight or gay. Probably bi. No question, this guy could fuck anyone.

Monday January 4, 1982

I spotted a tiny ad for it in the back section of the New York Native. It read: "Wall Street Sauna: A Man's Retreat." Sounded pretty gay to me. I told Jim I wanted to check it out after dinner. He said that was fine. I guess he thought that after almost nine years of monogamy a little taste of the real world wasn't such a bad idea. Actually, Jim cautioned me to play safe. He reminded me of that New York Times article from last July. Lawrence Altman reported 41 cases of a fatal rare cancer among gay men in New York City and San Francisco. That was sobering. Jim gave me a hug and told me to play safe and always use a condom. But I was all excited. I figured this was my first gay sauna. I could have a little fun and at least jerk off with some guy. So I put on my faded blue Levi's with no belt and my green bomber jacket. I grabbed my tiny popper bottle. My heart was pounding as a middle-aged guy checked me in at a tiny window that looked just like the ticket office for a seedy porno cinema. What a disappointment inside. The place was empty, except for a few trolls. It's probably only a lunch crowd. Afterall, Wall Street is deserted in the evening. The check-in guy sees me leaving after just fifteen minutes. Feeling guilty, he refunds my money. Plus, he tells me it's usually the busiest on Friday evenings before the weekend. Good tip. I thanked him. Walking back home I reflected on Jim's touching note of caution.

TUESDAY JANUARY 5, 1982

This diary thing is taking up a lot of time, but I'm getting into it. I mentioned the Wall Street Sauna (WSS) to Bob, my best friend at work. We both work at Skidmore, Owings and Merrill, you know, the elite corporate architects in Midtown. Bob has been at SOM three years already. I just arrived six months ago. Bob's a super cool guy, my buddy going back to Cornell. Back then we enjoyed some hot scenes together a few times. Since graduation in '74, Bob's been living with Dave in New York City. Dave's a banker. Bob and Dave have an open relationship. Jim and I mostly pretend we have a closed relationship. We have our secrets. Bob tells me he's been to WSS a few times; that figures, he's been around the block more than once. Bob fools around plenty. I'm jealous. But Bob is egoless. He never rubs it in my face. "You'll have fun there Miles. It's a friendly crowd." I told Bob I'm going to WSS on Friday. He'd join me, but Dave has already accepted a dinner invite.

WEDNESDAY JANUARY 6, 1982

First thing in the office, Bob tells me he feels badly about abandoning me at WSS on Friday. "Will you be alright Miles?" "No problem Bob, but thanks for asking. Want to join me at the Adonis after work tonight? They're showing Cadinot's latest porno flick Charmants Cousins. I heard it's fantastic."

"Fantastic" doesn't begin to cover it. Cousins is another Cadinot masterpiece. What a genius. It's filmed in the bucolic French countryside inside a romantic old barn. The boys are all hot and super sweet. Lots of dreamy dark shadows that make the warm sexy skin tones really glow. Reminds me of Caravaggio. Really beautiful.

THURSDAY JANUARY 7, 1982

I had a good workout at the Apple Gym tonight. Really pushed myself. Starting to feel a few muscles. It's pretty empty in the evenings. There's only one asshole, Mr. Pastey Face, who is apparently there every night doing deadlifts by himself with his sweat-stained leather belt. He loads the barbell up with hundreds of pounds of plates, then lifts it to his waist and drops the whole thing. The entire building shakes. Of course, he has an unattractive body, long stringy, oily hair and wears dorky gym clothes. He must be straight.

FRIDAY JANUARY 8, 1982

It's Friday. I'm back at WSS. The check-in guy remembers me. It's definitely better than Monday; there must be at least a dozen guys. After stripping down in the small locker room; I hit the showers with the open stalls. It's empty; I grab the one on the end.

A short chunky wrestler-type guy struts by my shower stall. He's thirtyish, Hispanic, shaved head, hairless brown skin, sexy beard stubble, tattoos on his chest and upper right arm. Looks like rough trade, maybe a construction guy; he definitely works out. A few seconds later, he reappears and stops right in front of my stall, then backs into the stall opposite mine. He's a cock tease. He's wearing a BIKE jock strap with a thin waist band, olive-colored, mesh pouch that clearly shows everything.

I'm turned-on 100%; I'm a jock strap queen. This guy's super-hot and he knows it. He's confident, raunchy, a little intimidating, the real thing. He squeezes the plump mesh crotch while facing me sideways. I'm rock hard. I remember Jim's words of caution. I stay in my stall and jerk off. I pop almost instantly. He gives me a little smile and a nod as he moves on without a word. As he slowly walks away, he makes sure I get a clear view of the white straps across his sexy brown butt. I don't mention any of this to Jim.

SATURDAY JANUARY 9, 1982

I woke up with cum on the sheets. I had a wet dream last night—the Hispanic guy from WSS was butt-fucking me in a shower stall. It was wonderful. He kept his jock strap on the whole time.

I'm thinking back on my jock strap guy. I'm lying nude in bed next to Jim asleep. I start rubbing Jim's back, squeezing his soft butt-cheeks. Jim moans softly, pressing his butt tight up against me. He moans louder. I lube up and let loose. I close my eyes. I picture the Hispanic's brown butt with the olive-colored jock strap. I cum an ocean.

SUNDAY JANUARY 10, 1982

I'm getting behind in my work at SOM. I'd better go in Sunday afternoon for a few hours. Of course, Bob is already there. He puts in huge amounts of overtime. His boss is a prick. Bob and I like to fool around, talk a little dirty, we're sex buddies. It all started back at Cornell in the design studio late at night. Tonight we work hard for three straight hours before we retire to the partner's rear conference room. I pull out the tube of lube. Bob is just waiting for me.

MONDAY JANUARY 11, 1982

It's been three days and I can't stop thinking about the cock tease at the WSS. I jerk-off every night just thinking about him. I'm definitely going back on this coming Friday.

TUESDAY JANUARY 12, 1982

I'd seen him before. Just outside the back service entrance to my building on tiny Ann Street. He hangs out begging at the top of the stairs to the subway entrance. I've passed him dozens of times on my way to SOM in the morning. He begs for money; looking for loose change from the Wall Street crowd.

For some reason, on this morning, I stopped dead in my tracks. Was it the winter sun hitting his rosy face? Maybe. He looked different. Sure, the same dirty clothes, the unkempt blond hair, the beard stubble. Today, in the sunlight his eyes were alive, a sapphire blue. The bone structure of his face was movie star material. In a gentler world, you'd say he was handsome, even gorgeous, just on bad times, a little dirty, that's all, but still gorgeous. I spoke first.

"Hi, I'm Miles. Let me buy you a hot breakfast at the coffee shop on the corner. You must be cold. It's freezing this morning. What's your name?" "I'm William. Call me Billy." "Sure thing Billy. Don't worry, the staff in the coffee shop is cool. I know them. They won't hassle you. Relax. Just stay by my side. Let's get you warmed up." We sat in a booth in a back corner. Billy looked tired, exhausted. He didn't speak. Hot coffee, sausage, eggs and a bowl of hot oatmeal helped. He started to relax, to come back to life.

I told him I lived in the building across the street, the Bennett Building. I asked Billy where he spends his nights; mostly in the back corners of subway stations or inside the trains. He doesn't feel safe in the city shelters. As I stared into Billy's eyes I felt a connection. He was probably about my age, just badly weathered. A gentle warm face, fragile and vulnerable. The fact that he seemed comfortable returning my stare equally told me he must be gay. It didn't matter, I was determined to help him, gay or straight. I thought about taking him upstairs for a hot shower in the loft, but I knew Jim would never approve. "Miles, you must be out of your mind."

I had an idea. I know our landlord Fred. He likes me; he always treats me like a son. He's Jewish, old school. Rents out tiny spaces in the Bennett Building to old Jewish jewelers who fled the Nazis. The empty top floors he rents illegally to us artists, about six of us, open artist lofts, all under the radar. He's cool. My idea is to hook up Billy with Fred. Get him a job, inside, out of the cold. Maybe a janitor. Maybe something more substantial, who knows, Billy could be an ex-stockbroker. It's possible, right? Then I decided, "Fuck Jim. He doesn't have to know. I'm taking care of Billy. Let him shave and shower. I can wash his clothes. He can wear my old clothes. Then I'll introduce him to Fred, explain the situation. I know Fred will help.

Fortunately, by the time Billy and I get to the loft, Jim has left for work. I decide this will be my secret. Once shaved and cleaned up, Billy looks terrific. He keeps thanking me. He's nervous. I give him a hug. I tell him to just relax. We go up to see Fred in his office upstairs. It's a small operation; just Fred and his wife Sadie who keeps the books. I introduce Billy as a "friend who needs help."

Fred understands immediately. "Yes, yes I've seen you on the sidewalk, good fellow. Thank you Miles, for bringing Billy to my attention. Forgive me for not reaching out to you sooner with a helping hand. But let me help you now. You need work, yes? Are you good with numbers? I sense you are. Why don't we try you out as an assistant to my wife Sadie? She could use your help with numbers. You need a place to stay I'm pretty sure. I have a small simple room on this floor that you can use until you get on your feet. Toilet in the hall. You're a lucky fellow Billy. Miles is a good man."

WEDNESDAY JANUARY 13, 1982

I decided not to mention Billy to Jim at all. He'll just get all upset. On the way to work I first check in with Fred. Sadie has been busy with city social services getting Billy help. He's meeting with his new social worker as we speak. His new room will be ready today so Billy will be able to sleep inside tonight. I'm extremely pleased.

THURSDAY JANUARY 14, 1982

I need to tell someone about Billy. I can't say a word to Jim. I proposed a lunch out of the office with Bob. He was blown away. "God Miles, that's really incredible. They should make you a saint. I always knew you were special, but I must say, this tops everything. Let me know how I can help. Eventually I want to meet Billy." I felt great! Who knows, maybe Billy will become a new friend.

Friday January 15, 1982

I was feeling horny. Must be all that good Samaritan work I've been up to lately. Anyway, I didn't tell Jim I'm going to WSS tonight. He thinks I'm going to the Apple. Once I'm in the basement, I strip down naked and check out the showers first. No sign of my chunky wrestler. Next, I go to the steam room. It's moderately busy. In the back corner I see somebody vaguely through the steam wearing a jock strap. Getting closer, I see it's him. This time he's in the classic white BIKE model. I immediately kneel down and give him a blowjob. I recall Jim told me blowjobs were safe; just butt-fucking requires a condom. I was relieved. Afterwards, he slaps my ass hard once with a loud sharp pop. It actually felt good. He was quite the stud. I'd never had such hot raunchy sex before. What a breakthrough! I've arrived.

Saturday January 16, 1982

I've been thinking about Billy all morning. He's my secret from Jim. I guess I have more than a bit of a crush on him. I keep playing the tape of Billy standing buck naked in my loft, dripping wet after his shower, beads of glistening water on his beautiful buttocks. I want to lick him dry. He covered himself with a towel. He's shy. Maybe he caught me staring. I can only guess he's gay. He just seems too sensitive and gentle to be straight. But I know for now we can't meet.

Sunday January 17, 1982

I picked up a couple of classic BIKE jock straps from Hudson's on Second Avenue. I really like the yellow ones. I tried one on in front of a full-length mirror. It's definitely hot. I'm ready for WSS.

Monday January 18, 1982

I decided to really push myself at the Apple. I worked out nonstop for three hours with protein drinks during breaks. Adam took notice. He started spotting for me regularly. Finally, I could start to really feel my muscles. They ached, but in a goodway. I must be making progress. I'm going to repeat this every day after work so I'll have something to show Mr. Jock Strap on Friday.

TUESDAY JANUARY 19, 1982

On my SOM lunch hour I went to the Barnes & Noble on Fifth Avenue to check out their books for men's exercise, specifically men's abdominals. I have a thing for six-pack abs. It started when I was five back in the men's locker room in Albuquerque. There was this trim athletic guy in the showers. An Adonis. His abdominal muscles were perfect, each one sharply defined. I wanted to touch them all, rub them hard with sudsy soap. Well, I've finally decided, I'm going to get my own set of six-pack abs.

WEDNESDAY JANUARY 20, 1982

I met Jim after work in Julius'. It's Jim's favorite gay bar in New York City. He likes to sit for hours drinking at the small window tables. He always orders a gin and tonic or red wine in a stem wine glass. I usually have only one beer in a bottle. I'm usually totally bored within fifteen minutes tops. Tonight I really just want to get to the Apple for my workout. But Jim loves it, the sawdust on the floor, the green glass light fixtures, the friendly neighborhood crowd. Jim knows all the bartenders by their first names. A skinny tall blond just walked in. He looks like he just stepped off the beach in California, a surfer beach bum. Jim gives him a friendly smile. The blond surfer smiles back.

THURSDAY JANUARY 21, 1982

I ran over to Alitalia on my lunch hour to pick up info on Venice. I always fly to Italy on Alitalia. The plane is usually full of Italians. I love listening to them speak. Italian is so musical. And then there are those Italian men onboard. I always look for them, checking out the goods in their tight Italian trousers. The Alitalia clerk was cute. He had a decent map of Venice. I'll get a better one once I get there. I'm leaving for Venice on Sunday. I have to start packing soon.

Friday January 22, 1982

It's Friday. I'm back at WSS. I'm hyper aroused as I set off to find Mr. Jock Strap. I walk the entire place three times. No sign of him anywhere. Disappointed, I dress and head back home empty handed. After all that hard work at the Apple he pulls a no-show. What a pisser! Jim isn't home from work yet. Frustrated, I pull out my favorite Colt magazine with photos of butch outdoor threesomes. I take a single hit from my popper hidden in the medicine cabinet, I jerk-off with just a few strokes.

I did some packing for Venice. I'll be leaving in just two days. It will be in the dead of winter. Nine full days there plus a day at each end traveling. The big deal is I'm going alone. Normally, Jim and I always vacation together. This time around I proposed going solo. Jim was surprised, but he quickly accepted my decision. Winter alone in Venice is bound to be a bit melancholy. I've been there more than half a dozen times, even once with Jim, but never in the dead of winter and this time, for some unknown reason, I want it to be solo. Sort of a Dirk Bogarde moment from Visconti's Death in Venice. That's all for now. Jim just walked in.

Saturday January 23, 1982

I woke up with an urge to see Billy. I just wanted to see him once before I left for Venice tomorrow. Just to make sure he's alright. I told Jim I was doing an early morning workout at Apple. I snuck up the back stair to the ninth floor with my gym bag. I knew Billy's room number, 907. I knocked softly. Billy opened the door slowly. "Miles, please come in." His radiant smile told me everything. Billy was fine. I hugged him. Billy hugged me back. "I just wanted to see how you are doing. I'm away for several weeks. Is everything okay?" "Yes, I'm fine. Thank you for everything Miles."

The small room was dominated by a huge tall double-hung window that framed the gray winter sky filled with light snow. A tiny desk at the window held a small green glass library lamp. Several library books were piled up neatly. They looked like books of poetry – I spotted several volumes I own. Ginsberg's epic poem Howl was open on the desk, it's bold black and white book jacket easy to read across the room. "I see you also love poetry. I love this poem in particular. I like to read it out loud. Can I read you a passage?" "Yes, if I can return the favor to you." We traded turns reading poetry, back and forth. It was very intimate, better than sex. Billy came alive. We read to each other in facing chairs for over an hour. I left knowing that Billy was fine. We hugged. He would be just fine while I was away.

SUNDAY JANUARY 24, 1982

Leave for Venice. Change planes in Rome. Flying Alitalia. Giuseppe, my seat mate, was extremely cute. It's hard to tell. All Italian men look gay to me. They lost my checked luggage. Should get it back by tomorrow.

MONDAY JANUARY 25, 1982

Hotel near La Fenice is basic. No problem. Great location. My missing luggage is delivered to my room as promised.

I walk to Piazza San Marco. It's magnificent. The church is dark and mysterious. I'm using Giulio Lorenzetti's classic 1926 guidebook with some dozen walks that crisscross the city.

Most restaurants are closed. The city is very empty. Dinner alone feels odd. Walk back to Piazza San Marco in the fog. It's deserted except for the sanitation guys in their tiny trucks and their sexy orange jump suits.

TUESDAY JANUARY 26, 1982

Santa Maria dei Miracoli is spectacular. The church abuts a canal on one whole side. Small piazza in front. Glorious wood barrel-vaulted ceiling. Covered inside and out with inlaid polychrome marbles. A Renaissance jewel.

Wednesday January 27, 1982

The damp cold is making my toes numb. Start wearing two pairs of socks. Maybe this explains why the locals have rosy red cheeks. Every day I make sure to send Jim a postcard. I miss him. At night in my narrow bed, I hear loud voices and the footsteps of party goers on the stone pavement. It's well past two in the morning.

Thursday January 28, 1982

Santa Maria Formosa. The favorite Renaissance church of my Cornell drawing instructor J.O. Mahoney. Greek-cross plan. Interior has a triptych by Bartolomeo Vivarini. I can understand why J.O. loves the place.

Friday January 29, 1982

I noticed him—a handsome young gondolier standing alone in the empty piazza at the edge of a small canal. His traditional straw hat was off, showing his thick black hair. His shiny black gondola was tight up against the stone landing steps. He was standing with one foot on the stone landing, the other on his boat. Most striking of all, was the long black oar in his hands, rising from the black water between his legs, deliberately crossing his crotch. He started to rub the oar against the crotch patch. First, just a bit, but soon more firmly, more deliberately. I was only twenty feet away on the church steps, but I could easily see the bulge through the soft patch.

I hesitated, briefly conflicted. Finally, as he ran the oar across the full length of his boner, I gave in. As I stood up, he nodded me over with a faint smile, stepped back a bit, inviting me on board. He sat me down just in front of him standing, my eye level directly across from his crotch.

It occurred to me, he had probably done all this before: the oar, the crotch, the invitation to board. But I couldn't care less; it was no problem; I was definitely all in. Afterall, I was on vacation right? It's not as if I planned it. It just happened. Anyway, I knew I needed this as much as I needed the air I breathe. I was hyper aroused. I realized I was about to have real sex with

19

an Italian stud. I'd never come even close to this in the nine years since I came out. Sex with Jim was boring. This guy looks super-hot. I was more than ready.

He rowed us around a corner into an even smaller deserted canal. At a sunny edge he secured the gondola and leaned back against his oars. The tiny silver buttons opened easily; the cloth was well worn. As I loosened the soft patch, I finally held his cock in my hands. It was magnificent in the sunlight. I swallowed it whole.

His hands were firmly on my head; his fingers running through my mussed hair while tracing my movements. I made love to his cock, to the thick beautiful shaft, to the firm head with its crisp pointed tip. All the time he moaned softly. Then he stopped me and forced me down on a cushion on my back centered in his boat. He pulled my trousers off and put my legs in the air resting against his beefy shoulders. He was planning to butt-fuck me. I was thrilled. This was what I always dreamed of. Jim never fucked me. My gondolier was fantastic. He started off slow taking his time, but finished with full force. He showed me the stars. Finally, at long last, real queer sex with an experienced lover. I had arrived. Thank God.

I felt cool air on my sweaty forehead. As he rowed us back, I listened to him singing softly. He had a clear voice, strong and expressive. Back at the tiny church piazza, we stepped onto the stone landing and shared a hug for a few brief seconds. His musky scent left my head buzzing. I realized I had just passed through a gay rite of passage, never to go back again. My life was changed forever.

SATURDAY JANUARY 30, 1982

Santa Maria della Visitazione. After yesterday's glorious gondolier, I'm in a trance. I feel an urge to see the vast oval ceiling fresco by Tiepolo in this church. The ceiling fresco is intensely sensual; it overwhelms me, just as the gondolier had. It depicts the Coronation of the Virgin, clad in white standing on a massive globe, being received into paradise by the figures of the Trinity: Christ holding his cross, the dove of the Holy Spirit and God the Father with a crown for the Virgin in his outstretched hands. All this is surrounded by angels in a vast sky of blues and smokey golds. Tiepolo transports me up into his heaven. The view is the perfect complement to my earthly encounter with the gondolier. He too welcomed me into paradise. But his was a hidden, shadowed masculine one. His canvas was equally thrilling, painted by touch and feel, by sound and murmur, by taste and smell.

Sunday January 31, 1982

I need some great architecture to occupy my confused mind. Palladio's Church of the Redentore on the Giudecca fits the bill. I took a water taxi. The design has a refreshing simplicity. It is considered Palladio's finest piece of religious architecture. I lucked out. I was able to sit through a Sunday Mass in the back. The choral music was just what I needed.

Monday February 1, 1982

San Giovanni Grisostomo. The small pretty church was totally empty except for a very young priest busy on the main altar. As I approached him he must have heard my footsteps and turned backwards to see me. He smiled. He was busy arranging, then rearranging, the candles and flowers. Finally finished, he turned back once again, as if to check me out more carefully. He was licking his lips nervously. Was he cruising me? First a horny gondolier, now an equally horny Catholic priest.

I stared at his trim backside. I found him increasingly erotic. I imagined what was hidden within the folds of his black robes, a soft enthralling rump, a deep delicious crack, a tender silky anus. The noon bells announced afternoon closing. He paused to see if I would be staying or leaving. I remained seated; he had me under his spell. He locked the main door and walked to the vestry. I followed.

Inside the vestry he locked the door, opened his black robes, exposing his pearly white butt. It was gorgeous and plump, inviting and ripe. The lad leaned over the massive central table; his arms fully outstretched. I understood his naughty request immediately. I butt-fucked him standing upright at the table's edge. He moaned loudly at first, then softly while lost in deepest pleasure. I smiled. We made the perfect queer pair of lovers, a horny American tourist and a wayward Catholic priest.

TUESDAY FEBRUARY 2, 1982

Last full day in Venice. I woke up with a morning glory. I'm feeling melancholy at the thought of leaving behind all these beautiful Italian studs. I made a return visit to San Marco to see once more the undulating stone floor from centuries of flooding. The gold mosaics were gorgeous. Back at the hotel I packed.

WEDNESDAY FEBRUARY 3, 1982

Return flight to New York City. I have a boner for most of the trip. I keep replaying details of the Venetian sex tapes in my head. They have somehow all merged into one erotic threesome.

I get home to the loft about three in the afternoon. Jim has a special dinner on the stove. All my Venetian postcards are in a long line on the kitchen cookbook shelf. Seeing them there, Venice looks so insignificant, banished to a shelf. It feels so distant; like it's in another universe. Jim is also distant. After dinner he tells me he has some "important news."

Seated across from me at the tiny breakfast table, Jim tells me in one fell swoop: that while I was away in Venice, he fell in love with someone in Julius', the attraction is all consuming and he will be moving out on Saturday. Our relationship is over. All this, after nine years of living together, sharing everything, in a safe monogamous relationship. I'm stunned. After a few awkward moments, Jim left to spend the night with my replacement, a 25-year-old disco bunny named Sandy. Suddenly, I'm all alone. I call no one.

I reflect back on Venice. Was Venice solo, a huge mistake? No, absolutely not. My gondolier and my priest saved me. They were both passionate lovers, not afraid to show me their love. They woke me up. I crave their passion now. I lust for their salty skin, their sweet oily sweat, their musky Venetian aromas. I jerk off just thinking of them—their playful eyes, their swollen cocks, their soft inviting butts. I collapse on the bed, exhausted, dreaming fondly of Italian cock up my ass. I smiled, I chuckled, I thanked God. I felt reborn.

THURSDAY FEBRUARY 4, 1982

I awoke in a state of wonder. I felt light headed. Back in the office I returned to earth and told my work buddy Bob about my two Venetian lovers. "Miles you look fantastic. I'm jealous." Then, when I told him that Jim checked out almost immediately upon my return, Bob wasn't even that surprised. He told me he saw it coming. "Jim was getting old. He's going through his mid-life crisis. It happens all the time, especially to gay guys." Perhaps Bob was right. Jim is nine years older than me, he's forty. The guy he fell for is a disco queen, some fifteen years younger. The guy probably makes Jim feel young again. I always thought Jim and I would grow old together on some park bench looking back on our shared lives. Like in the Simon and Garfunkel song Old Friends. He clearly has other plans. But a 25-year-old disco bunny? How does that compute?

FRIDAY FEBRUARY 5, 1982

I decided I'm definitely going to the WSS tonight, I need a physical distraction. I crave some rough sex. I could fuck anything and I want to find some horny stud to fuck me long and hard. I found both. First, I'm cruising in the hallway and stop at this naked Black dude. He smiles as he sees me staring at his bubble butt. "You want some?" I place my hand on his butt. He grabs my hard cock and leads us to a private toilet room, locks the door, leans over the sink and asks me to butt-fuck him. I really let him have it big time. I yell out, "Take that Jim, you fucking asshole!" The guy didn't even notice. Then afterwards in the steam room I spot old Mr. Jock Strap. This time he's buck naked, showing off his giant Hispanic boner. I boldly approach him, placing my hand on his cock. "Fuck me hard, you horny stud. And use a condom." He takes the bait and pounds me long and hard. I don't want it to end. I let him have everything he wants. I want him to leave nothing of me behind, to fuck me until I'm no more than a pool of spent cum.

SATURDAY FEBRUARY 6, 1982

I awoke numb. It's Jim's moving-out day. Sandy and a friend came along to help lift boxes. This is the first time I've seen Sandy up close, although he looks familiar. Then it clicks, he's the surfer from Julius'. Tall and lanky, shoulder length hair, a dirty blond. Jim does the introductions. He introduces Sandy as "my beautiful hippie lover." He's certainly cute. I can see why Jim fell for him. He's sexy like a flower child. Friendly enough, but keeps pretty much to himself. He looks kind of empty upstairs. Jim told me earlier he's a famous gay DJ. He's apparently a great dancer; he lives for the dance floor.

The task at hand mostly comes down to packing up Jim's clothes, special kitchen pots and pans, his classical music records and his cherished art pottery. He will come back later for the tons of books. We settle the division of things easily without any arguments.

Jim announces that he and Sandy plan on moving to the San Francisco Castro in late July. That will give them plenty of time. Jim tells me I must come to the Saint next Saturday. Sandy is a member and I'm welcome to be his guest. He'll leave my name at the door. Jim thinks that it will be good for me to dance in the crowd and meet new faces. "It might liberate you." Do I need to be liberated? Maybe he's right. It just seems rather abrupt. I'm still totally confused. I go for a walk in City Hall Park. I can't stand seeing the loft in a total mess. When I return, thankfully, they are all gone. I clean up for over an hour, rearrange things so there's no trace of what has just happened. I'm alone and I'm exhausted.

Sunday February 7, 1982

All day I've been thinking about Jim and Sandy. I can see they're totally in love. I haven't seen Jim look so alive in years. He's really gone off the deep end: new lover, quits his job, moves to the Castro, turns into a disco bunny, reinvents himself at middle age. I wish them well. They are living their dream as two brave gay men.

By early evening I was getting lonely. I kept thinking about the backroom at The International Stud. Jim's college buddy Gordon introduced me to it a year ago. It was really raunchy. I haven't been back since. So, I end up in the dark with a pack of sex-starved guys giving blowjobs, trading off cocks as if they were at a wine tasting. But it was just what I needed tonight, some of the good stuff.

Monday February 8, 1982

I have a one-track mind. All day long at SOM, all I could think about was last night's sex at the Stud. I craved more. Then I recalled the 59th Street IRT Station at Bloomingdale's. Bob had told me when I started working at SOM that it was an active tearoom. I decided to check it out over my lunch hour. Inside was this middle-aged bald guy in leather chaps over ripped blue jeans. Perfect. "Hi, I'm Miles. Want some head?" "Sure kid, I'm Helmut." He was built like a brick shithouse. He fit my sex fantasies perfectly. He loosened his thick belt and pulled out his massive cock. He let me blow him nice and slow. I was in heaven. Back at my desk, I kept replaying the blowjob. By 5:10 pm I was back in the tearoom, ready for round two with Helmut. He must have known I'd be coming back. Afterwards he handed me a black card with his name and number. I put it in safe keeping in a box on my desk.

Tuesday February 9, 1982

Wait a minute. Time to slow down. Take stock of the situation. What the hell am I doing? This can't just go on and on. The saunas, the baths, the backrooms, the tearooms. Seems like ever since Venice I've been on fire. Sex on the brain. Jim's leaving is obviously connected. He knew this would happen. He encouraged my going to the WSS. He even told me to play safe. There are so many things I don't understand. I'm really ripe for some therapy, some psychotherapy I mean. Bob saw Terrence a few years ago and said it really helped him. I need help. I'm a wreck. I'm exhausted. I'll never figure this all out on my own. I'll call Terrence tomorrow. Set up something asap.

Wednesday February 10, 1982

Jim called tonight out of the blue. I was stunned. It's only one week since we last talked, since he walked out the door. I was speechless. His voice was gentle and calm. He said he just wanted to check in on me, to make sure I'm alright. I started crying. "There, there Miles. I'm sorry you're crying. You'll be okay, trust me, you'll be okay." I thanked Jim for calling and went to bed early.

Thursday February 11, 1982

I'm excited. Tonight, was my first private therapy session with Terrence. I like him. He's a good match. Gay, in his forties, warm, butch, bald, very masculine. He's actually hot. That could be a problem. We'll see. I'll certainly be comfortable being open with him, sharing my deepest secrets. Isn't that what therapy is all about? Digging deeper, new discoveries, new insights? God knows I have my work cut out for me. Terrence gave me an assignment for the week. What are my goals? What do I want to get out of therapy? Good start. I'll have to give that a lot of thought.

Friday February 12, 1982

I was a little anxious about going back to WSS after what happened last week. But I was all alone in the loft tonight and I needed a distraction, so I gave in. It was a snowy night. The place was jumping. In the locker room a friendly Black guy put the make on me. "Come here often? I've seen you here before. You're getting some nice upper body definition. I'm Wolf. I'm a grad student at New York University, business administration. I like to come down here to get away from fellow students and faculty." "Hi Wolf, I'm Miles. I live in the neighborhood. I'm an architect." "That's cool.

Could I interest you in a little fun in the steam room? I think you're really hot." "Sounds great. I assume you're a top, right? I'm fine with either." "Yep, I'm a top. Don't worry, I always use a condom. I've had my eye on your gorgeous white butt for weeks! You're driving me crazy!" With that open declaration I put my hand on his massive cock for a squeeze. He was rock hard. "Don't worry. I promise you I'll go nice and slow. Just tell me what you want and when." He was true to his word. What a butt-fucker. He reminded me of my gondolier. We carried on in the steam room for half an hour. Wolf was super-gentle but "definitely substantial." They say Black cock up the butt is the best. Wolf was a real gentleman. I asked him for his number.

SATURDAY FEBRUARY 13, 1982

Tonight is my introduction to the Saint. I decided to take Sandy up on his offer. Jim told me the whole routine: an early, high-protein dinner, nap until 1 pm, shower, get out the disco wear, take a protein drink, grab a small popper bottle, then taxi over to the old Fillmore East on Second Avenue and 6th Street arriving after 2 pm. Plan on staying to daybreak with pancakes at the all-night diner around the corner. The music is always loud, so bring earplugs. Plan on being soaked in sweat. The balcony is strictly for anonymous sex, not socializing. Members have access to the showers afterwards. Expect plenty of action.

By the time I arrived I was totally psyched. As I opened the glass door into the vast dimly lit foyer, I could feel the whole floor shaking from 3,000 sweat-soaked guys dancing together under the open metal-domed ceiling. Her Highness Donna Summer, the Queen of Disco, sang high notes over everything else, wailing out her disco hits: Bad Girls and Dim All the Lights. I hardly knew anyone other than Jim and Sandy. It didn't matter at all. It was tribal, dancing shirtless with my brothers, showing off the goods, lost in the million points of light from the star machine. It was beautiful. I wished I had someone to share it all with.

Much later, in the balcony, I let a total stranger practically rape me. I gladly surrendered. He was a young Rumanian surgeon-in-training, a total sex fiend, who knew male anatomy in great detail. He fucked me in ways I never dreamed of, like some hot porno star covering all the bases. We left together for pancake breakfast. His name was Andrei. We talked about how they make those nesting Russian painted eggs. When it came time to part, he handed me his card and asked me to call him for a "fuck date." I made sure the card ended up in the box on my desk next to Helmut's and Wolf's.

Sunday February 14, 1982

Valentine's Day. I was dreading it. I was so happy when Angie accepted my last-minute invitation for dinner at the Finish restaurant Aquavit on East 55th. I knew it was one of her favorites. Sophisticated interior, classic modern furniture and Scandinavian chandeliers. Pure Angie.

She showed up on time, dressed all in black with her stunning gold necklace. "So, where's Jim?" I hadn't seen Angie since before I went to Venice. "We broke up." Her jaw dropped. Angie had known Jim and I since we arrived in New York City over six years ago. She knew we did everything together. Immediately, she understood. "Maybe it was that solo trip to Venice." I poured out the scene of my return, Jim's stunning announcement. "Maybe it's for the best. When my first marriage ended, I finally felt like myself."

Clearly upset, I told her I had always wished I could somehow propose marriage to her, but I knew that was impossible. I am a perfect 6 on Kinsey's scale of homosexuality, 100% homo. Suddenly Angie stood up, pulled me out of my chair and gave me a big hug. I started crying in front of everyone. A waiter appeared at my side with several extra linen napkins. As we sat back down, several fellow diners actually started to applaud. I turned beet red.

The rest of the meal we talked only about Venice. We both craved the escape. I described the wood barrel-vaulted ceiling at Santa Maria dei Miracoli, the Tiepolo ceiling fresco at Grisostomo, Palladio's perfect Redentore, the undulating stone floors at San Marco. I always love sharing stories of Italy with Angie. She loves Italy as much as I do. When I finally confessed my sex encounters with the gondolier and the priest, Angie was in tears laughing. Angie's Jewish, she has a healthy attitude when it comes to sex.

The meal was superb. The presentations are always over-the-top. Angie was magnificent. Afterwards, I walked Angie home to her apartment in Kips Bay. It was a lovely evening, my first in a very long while.

MONDAY FEBRUARY 15, 1982

I already missed Andrei. I'm so needy. I craved his attention. I called him up first thing once I got to the office. He was really glad I called. He'd been thinking about the sex we had at the Saint in the balcony. I told him I was free tonight if he wanted to get together. "Absolutely! You got it Miles." I felt a lot better. My anxiety vanished. I had something to look forward to. Andrei came by my loft right after work. He showed up in an old motorcycle jacket. It was super-hot. He was about to take it off when I asked him to fuck me with just the jacket on, nothing else. "Sure thing. I like the idea. Lucky me!" Afterwards, I asked Andrei if I could just try on his jacket. He said sure. I decided right then and there that I was going to buy a motorcycle jacket tomorrow.

TUESDAY FEBRUARY 16, 1982

I love it. Finally, my first real motorcycle jacket. It came from Hudson's in the East Village. It's actually pretty heavy. Thick black leather, not shiny, nice dull finish. Snug fit. I like the collar raised. Epaulets, zipped pockets, silver snap buttons, silver rivets. The works. It's terrific. My new look for cruising.

WEDNESDAY FEBRUARY 17, 1982

All day long at work all I could thing about was cruising in my new motorcycle jacket. I even left work an hour early so I could change at the loft before heading over to Christopher Street. I wore my ripped faded Levi's, a white tee and work boots. I figured I'd take Christopher to the river and hit the empty trucks in the Meat Packing District. I was looking for a leatherman hot for some action. As I hopped into the first truck all I saw were a couple of joggers screwing doggy-style in the back. The bottom still had his jock strap on. The top was naked, butt-fucking his friend while pulling the jock straps way back, releasing them together with a sharp pop. The bottom's butt was turning rosy red. I jerked off just watching them. The top smiled at me. I smiled back. I walked back to the loft and went to bed early.

THURSDAY FEBRUARY 18, 1982

Second therapy session with Terrence. I purposely wore my new motorcycle jacket. I don't know why exactly. I wanted Terrance to see me in it. He noticed it immediately. "Nice jacket. Looks brand new." I told him how I just bought it after years of dreaming about it. He asked me a lot of questions about the jacket.

"Why get the jacket now?" I'm not sure. I really need it now. Maybe because I'm feeling vulnerable after Jim dumped me. I feel stronger wearing it.

"How do you feel when you put on the jacket?" Butch, strong, masculine, safe, in control.

"Say you're in a regular cotton navy windbreaker, how do you feel?" Ordinary, nobody special, kind of weak, not sexy, a little feminine, not in control.

"Are you a sissy?" I really hate that label! Don't call me a sissy! I'm not a sissy! The playground bully called me a sissy in front of everyone. He made me cry.

"Sorry Miles, I won't ever call you a sissy again. I apologize Miles. Who else, besides me and the playground bully, called you a sissy?" My mother Terry would always mock me by saying, 'Miles, don't be such a sissy.' I hated that. I hated her for saying that to me. I was just a little kid. She was my mother; she should have known better.

30

"Why do you think she called you a sissy?" I think she looked at me and all she saw was a skinny weak shy kid who she thought was a sissy, a homo, a fag. I scared her. She didn't want a homo in her family.

"Why do you say that?" She sent me away to a Catholic boy's summer camp when I was eleven. Nobody had ever been sent to summer camp in my family. Never. I was lonely. No friends. I hated it. I think she thought it would make me tough, force me to play team sports, turn me into a hetero. She was wrong. I fooled her. I discovered the leather workshop. That's where I spent all my free time. Making pretty things out of black leather. No wonder I like black leather motorcycle jackets.

"Tell me what you like about black leather motorcycle jackets?" They're butch. God, I love them. I first noticed them in the movie The Wild One starring Marlon Brando. He was my hero. Tough, butch, nobody would dare call him a sissy.

"When do you plan on wearing your new jacket? All the time? Or only on special occasions?" Both. I'd like to. Probably not to work though. It might cause a scene. Now that I'm on my own, I feel safer in it. It's like my coat of armor. I'll wear it all the time at night when I'm out alone, you know, cruising. I wore it last night while I was cruising the trucks.

"Cruising? You mean looking for sex, sex with other men?" Yes.

"In the trucks in the Meat Packing District? How was it?" Hot. I just watched, I just jerked off. Two joggers were butt-fucking. The bottom's jock strap was super-hot. The top kept snapping the elastic bands hard against his butt, over and over, loud pops.

"How did you feel when you were cruising in your motorcycle jacket?" Fantastic! I just got it, it's a little early to say. But I think I'll really like it. It makes me feel alive and sexy.

Then I realized I'd completely forgotten to mention my trip to the Saint

31

and the sex in the balcony with the young surgeon Andrei. I told Terrence everything, especially the part of my wanting Andrei to rape me in the balcony. He was most interested in that.

"Why did you surrender yourself so easily to Andrei's desires?" I wanted a lover to dominate me. Jim never did. He was always so passive, the bottom. I wanted a top to find me attractive, to want to fuck the living daylights out of me. Andrei did that. He was really into me for some reason. He was an animal. I found his lust a turn-on.

"So, you'd say it was a positive experience?" Yes, absolutely.

"Just remember that Miles. Andrei craved your body." I hugged Terrence. My time was up.

FRIDAY FEBRUARY 19, 1982

After work, I went straight home. Early supper and some reading. I kept thinking about everything Terrence said. I fell asleep in my clothes.

SATURDAY FEBRUARY 20, 1982

Douglas lives alone. Above me on the top floor in a corner loft of the Bennett Building. He was around the day Jim and Sandy were moving out, so he knows Jim and I broke up. He's seven years older than me, super-butch, shaved head. Plus, Douglas always wears a black leather jacket.

That evening, I was returning home late from the Eagle. I had struck out. I was still dressed for sex in my faded Levi's and my new motorcycle jacket. As I waited for the freight elevator, Douglas suddenly appeared. He was returning from a late-night run. He often did that sort of thing; he's a night owl. He was in running shorts covered in sweat. I saw him staring at my crotch. "Let's go up."

We stepped into the old cab with its rough wood floor. I let him take charge. He closed the metal gate. I noticed he pressed his floor 11, skipping my floor 7. It was a long slow ride up in silence as we listened to the hum of the motor, keeping count of the clicking sound at each floor. Finally on level 11 it stopped abruptly shaking the whole cab. Douglas opened the sliding gate just an inch or two which locked the elevator in place.

He ripped open my Levi's fly. I handed him my boner. I then rebuttoned the top buttons to give myself a tight denim cock ring. Douglas obviously liked what he saw. What a cocksman, plus his shaved head was a real turn-on.

He paused and looked up. "Do me with those Levi's on." Douglas pulled down his running shorts exposing his gorgeous butt and leaned over into a back corner. I slipped on the condom in the pocket of my motorcycle jacket. Douglas groaned audibly with pleasure as I started to fuck him real slow. The elevator gate squeaked with each thrust. I gave him all I had. I was so hyper-excited, I exploded in a minute.

Douglas turned around, his face flush with a cute grin. "Thanks kid. Hope that makes up a little for Jim and the bars." We said good night with a hug. I closed the noisy gate and pressed button 7.

SUNDAY FEBRUARY 21, 1982

Sunday morning I was all relaxed thinking back on my encounter with Douglas last night in the elevator. I really like Douglas a lot, but he's not interested in a relationship. He likes to sample a different lover every night. So I went for a long run around the tip of Battery Park. An early dinner and straight to bed.

Monday February 22, 1982

My buddy Bob from SOM came down to my loft for dinner. His lover Dave is away on business. I made a carbonara pasta dish. I filled Bob in on my recent highs and lows. It's been a roller coaster. He's a good listener. Bob really enjoyed hearing about my recent elevator sex with Douglas. He wanted all the details. I told him I'd look into a possible threesome with Douglas.

Out of the blue, Bob brought up Billy. "Hey Miles, what ever happened with that guy you helped out? His name was Billy right?" "He's doing fine. Gosh, it's already been a month and a half. I ran into Fred recently, and apparently, the bookkeeping job is working out fine. It's low stress. Turns out Billy was a burned-out commodities analyst on Wall Street. Isn't it crazy? Billy's probably smarter than all of us put together." "Hey look Miles, I really want to meet him. You could use a good distraction. Why don't both of you come over to my place on Friday after work for dinner? Dave will still be away on business for the Dutch bank. Better to keep it small, don't you think?" "You're right Bob, I could use a distraction. And you're right, smaller is better. I'll bring Billy personally so he's more comfortable confronting your fancy Central Park West doorman.

Tuesday February 23, 1982

I wanted to check in on Billy before we saw Bob on Friday. Just give him the backstory on Bob. I really want them to become friends. I sensed Billy could use a few friends. When I knocked on his door 907, there was no answer, so I left a note.

Wednesday February 24, 1982

Seven o'clock sharp there was a soft tap on my door. It must be Billy. In my note I had asked him to stop by my loft tonight. I just wanted to talk to somebody. I'm too lonely. I guess Billy is as well. We talked for hours. He told me his life story, growing up in rural Texas, then top of his class at Yale Law School, coming out in New York, his addiction to backroom sex clubs, losing control of his life, ending up on the street. I could tell he really wanted to share it all with me. Get a load off his mind. He trusted me completely. I felt flattered. I could see life returning to his face slowly as he talked nonstop. We started laughing, telling each other jokes, dirty stories. Billy has a beautiful smile. I told him all about Jim, our nine years together, our good years, our limited sex routine, our recent breakup following my solo trip to Venice. I even shared all the juicy details from my sex adventures in Venice with the gondolier and the Catholic priest. He made me laugh. He labeled me the "Horny American." By the time Billy said good night at eleven o'clock, I felt like I'd gained a new brother. I guess I had.

THURSDAY FEBRUARY 25, 1982

Third therapy session with Terrence. I mostly talked and talked. Terrence kept asking me questions, lots of them.

"So Miles, what is your goal in these therapy sessions?" I'm kind of vague. It definitely has to do with my breakup with Jim. I want to better understand what happened. I've suddenly gone from being isolated in a closed monogamous relationship for nine years to being on my own playing the field. It's scary, a little crazy. I feel out of control. I feel alive for the first time. But I feel like a slut. I'm fuckin' around like a slut. First at the WSS and then in Venice. And I shouldn't forget to mention the backroom at the Stud or the subway tearoom or Douglas in the elevator. Plus, there's Andrei in the balcony of the Saint. That was really intense. God, I must sound like such a slut.

"OK. Calm down Miles. It's fine. Let's start with the sauna first. You said the WSS, right? You went there for sex with men?" Yes, Jim thought it was a good idea. He encouraged it. I met a Hispanic guy there. I don't even know his name. We didn't talk. We just had kinky sex. He was very hot, into jock straps, which I am also. I loved it. What a change from Jim.

"How so?" Jim was always Mr. Uptight, Mr. Ivy League Princeton. He'd never talk about sex. Jim, talk dirty? Forget it. Sex with Jim was predictable, pretty boring after a while. The guy at the sauna was hot, confident, a sex stud. I really liked him.

"How often did you have sex with him?" Three times total. Then he vanished. First time just J.O. Then I sucked him off. The last time was the most intense. He fucked the daylights out of me in the steam room. I loved it. I'm such a slut, don't you think?

"I wouldn't go that far. Horny, most definitely, a slut, not so much." That's when I decided to tell Terrence about my dream. Ever since the elevator sex with Douglas a week ago, I've been having this recurring dream. It's very erotic. I always wake up with of pool of cum on my stomach.

"Tell me about your dream Miles. Where are you in the dream? Just close your eyes and take a few deep breaths. Relax. Take us back to your dream. Yes, that's it, take us back. Where are you in the dream?"

"I'm always in the backroom of the Stud. But it's not pitch dark, not completely, there are a few bare red lightbulbs in the ceiling. I can see figures in the soft red light. The room is packed tight full of leathermen having an orgy. The leather has a beautiful reddish sheen from the lights. I hear guys moaning. Maybe I'm in hell, but no, it looks more like heaven, heaven for guys like me. I'm all alone watching a kneeling leatherman from behind. I can't see his face. He's giving a cute Puerto Rican kid a terrific blowjob. He somehow senses I'm watching him. He stops, turns around slowly to face me. It's Douglas. He smiles, but doesn't speak. He immediately takes my hardon in his mouth. He looks up at me. His moist eyes are warm and loving. I feel safe. My fingers are all over his moustache, it's thick and bushy, wet from his saliva as he devours my cock whole. His eyes are closed. He's moaning softly. He takes his time. He pauses, looks up at me, his eyes now open. I can feel his love. He smiles again, then he works the head extra hard. The tip is hard as stone. It explodes. His tongue demands more. I cum again. He drains me completely. I cradle his bald head in my arms. I'm kissing the top of Douglas's head, his smooth shiny bald head. I wake up sweaty, warm cum all over my stomach.

"Wow! Sounds like a really wonderful dream Miles. You have a very active libido. That's a good thing. I wouldn't worry about it at all. Many guys would be jealous, including me Miles. Let's have a hug." Terrence gave me a long tight hug, the best.

"Now then, you said something about Venice. It also sounded like a dream. But it was real, correct? You went to Venice alone, right? What happened there?" I wanted to go alone, experience the fog, the winter light, study the art and architecture. I love Venice. I've been there many times, even once with Jim.

"What happened there? Did you have an adventure?" I told Terrence in great detail all about the Venetian gondolier and the Catholic priest. He let me talk and talk. Once I got started, I wanted to share every moment with him.

"Sounds like you had a really wonderful time. Would you agree?" Absolutely, I loved it. I opened up sexually. I felt completely alive. It was thrilling. I didn't want to go home. I didn't want to go back to my boring routines with Jim.

"I'd say your Venetian trip opened a new chapter in your life. A new beginning. A rebirth. Would you agree? I'd go so far as to say you showed real courage and love. I'm proud of you Miles." Of course, I started to cry. Terrence gave me another long hug while I cried like a baby.

"Now tell me about the real Douglas. You mentioned something about an elevator. Did you have an encounter in an elevator with Douglas?" You guessed it. It was fantastic. It just happened a couple of days after our last therapy session, before my recurring dream at the Stud. It was my first real sex while wearing my new motorcycle jacket. It was super-hot. I gave Terrence all the details.

"I can see you really had a great time with Douglas. He sounds like a really nice guy. He obviously cares a great deal about you." Absolutely. He's a true friend.

"Do you think you will have sex with Douglas again?" I don't know. If the opportunity presented itself, I doubt I'd be able to say no. I'm sure I'd say yes. I'm such a slut. I find Douglas really hot. He's older, experienced, a real leatherman. I'm really attracted to him.

"So, would it be fair to say Douglas is your "sex buddy?" Yes it would. That's precisely right. He's my new sex buddy. We look out for each other. He's not my boyfriend or full-time lover, but he's definitely my sex buddy. I never mentioned Andrei or my sex with him at my loft. It was my only secret from Terrence. I guess I figured Andrei was just another fuck buddy on the go, while yes, Douglas was a sex buddy for sure, but much more than that, he was a real friend for life.

That's it for today. Terrence wants to start with the 'slut' question first thing next week.

FRIDAY FEBRUARY 26, 1982

When I picked up Billy after work he looked so excited. He also looked very hot. He was wearing sneakers, faded blue jeans and a leather motorcycle jacket. What a pleasant surprise. Not only that, the jacket looked identical to the one I was wearing! "Nice jacket Billy. You're very cute. Hudson's, right?" He turned beet red with an enormous smile on his face. I was touched. I could tell he was really looking forward to spending the evening with Bob and me.

Wasting no time, he addressed the obvious question first. "I'm 100% gay." Relieved, I said "Thank God! We wouldn't want to share you with the straights." Bob added, "Ditto." Billy blushed. At Bob's dining table over Chinese takeout, Billy slowly opened up for Bob like he had with me several days earlier. He told more stories of his previous fast-lane life, by day an aggressive Wall Street trader, by night a gay sex club addict. The intense pressure, the insatiable sex, his nervous breakdown and finally ending up homeless. Bob gave Billy a warm hug. Under his weathered exterior was a beautiful loving man. We just wanted to take care of him.

Actually, I wanted to do a lot more than that. I wanted to make love to him. But he's doing surprisingly well on his own. He'll be fine. Fred and Sadie are the best thing for him now; they have already made him a son. He doesn't need a lover.

At the end of the evening, Bob boldly asked Billy if he'd be interested in a walk-thru visit of the Ramble across the street. "That's very tempting Bob. In the past I'd never hesitate, but tonight I think I'll pass. I don't want to spoil two wonderful new friendships."

Saturday February 27, 1982

I was feeling really horny again. Big surprise right? I started thinking about the Stud and then I recalled my last session with Terrence. Seems like all I talked about were my endless escapades with strangers. I decided to stay in for a change. I called up Billy for a movie date. He suggested Terms of Endearment playing in the Village. We had a great time and we didn't even have sex. A first.

Sunday February 28, 1982

Douglas called me up. He proposed a "fuck date" tonight in his loft around seven o'clock if I'm up for it. Just the two of us. Since I was such a good boy last night, I decided I deserved a reward. So I told Douglas yes definitely. It will be my first sex date with Douglas. After our spontaneous elevator sex, I have been thinking about him a lot. I guess he has as well.

Douglas has always lived alone. He likes to screw around too much to have a full-time lover. Like this thing tonight, it's typical; he just feels like getting his rocks off, so he calls me up. No big deal. I wish I could be so relaxed around sex. With me, everything's always a big deal.

His loft is masculine. In the middle are a pair of huge worn black leather sofas. There are pairs of vintage green glass library lamps. On the wall are several giant Mapplethorpe black and white photographs of black male body builders. Books everywhere. Douglas is the editor of a high-brow art criticism quarterly. He won the MacArthur Fellowship Award they give out to geniuses.

The main thing I noticed was the old sex sling hanging in the corner bay window. I knew Douglas frequented leather bars. Jim and I'd seen him in one years ago. He was dressed in full leather drag. Now I understand what he was looking for. Douglas saw me staring at his sling. "Want a ride buddy?" "You bet." I asked him to leave on his motorcycle jacket, unzipped. He fully understood my fantasy and gladly obliged.

I told him it was my first time in a sling and I really wanted to satisfy him 100%. He positioned me perfectly on my back like a pro. He started off real gentle and slow; after I relaxed, he gradually picked things up. Douglas was fantastic. I thought back fondly on my gondolier and priest in Venice, with Andrei at the Saint, with Wolf in the Wall Street Sauna. They were all fantastic lovers, passionate and intense. I'm a lucky man.

I told Douglas it was the best butt sex I'd ever had. It made my sex with Jim look pretty pathetic. He was flattered. He said I did great for my first time in a sling. "As good as any leatherman." Wow! What a compliment. Douglas asked if we could maybe get together again sometime soon. He's eager to show me some new positions. I said absolutely, anytime. I asked if he'd be interested in a threesome sometime in the future with Bob. He said sure.

MONDAY MARCH 1, 1982

Late afternoon at SOM, I was drawing at my desk. I was unable to concentrate. My brain kept returning to Douglas. When he picked up my phone call he chuckled, "I was hoping you'd give me a call today." Before I could even propose getting together, he beat me to it. "Miles, would you please be my 'butt boy' tonight?" Needless to say it was even more intense. Afterwards we showered together like two kids.

Tuesday March 2, 1982

It has been over three weeks since I saw Jim when he packed up his things and moved out of the loft. I was more than a little nervous about seeing him tonight. The dinner date in the backroom of Jane Street Seafood was Jim's idea. We used to eat there together all the time. The familiar setting, with just the two of us was a good idea.

Jim and Sandy won't be leaving for San Francisco for at least several months. Sandy can always DJ at the Saint. Eventually they'll be driving a U-Haul truck cross-country. I feel sorry for them. It sounds awful. But Jim doesn't care, he's excited, obviously he's completely in love. It's nice to see him so alive.

Jim is concerned about me. He asks me lots of questions. I just told him I'm doing fine and not to worry. I'll be alright. I told him about Terrence. Jim never put much stock in therapy. He can't open up like I do. I asked him about his job prospects in San Francisco. Not a lot of book publishers there. They're all in New York City. Jim's not concerned. Something will turn up.

We traded stories from the Saint. I enjoyed listening to Jim go on and on about the various disco characters. The DJ gossip, the endless intrigue. It reminded me of the old dynamic between us which Jim enjoyed so much and which I silently tolerated. Jim insisted I go to the Saint this coming Saturday as an early send off. I can tell it means a lot to him, so I agreed. I did enjoy my last visit, especially the sex in the balcony with Andrei. I didn't mention any of that to Jim of course. He would think I'm out of control again, a slut. And then there's Douglas. Jim met Douglas years ago. He'd be stunned if he knew Douglas and I have become "fuck buddies." That will be my secret.

I realize our paths have diverged already. As I explore new sexual frontiers for the first time, I feel my rebirth. I realize there is a wonderful big world beyond Jim, full of sexy gay men who I get to play with and love for the first time in my life. Finally, I'm inside the candy store. I'm scared, but excited. I too feel alive, like Jim does. As I part with Jim, I wish him well. I know we'll always remain good friends, but our worlds will be far apart.

Wednesday March 3, 1982

After work I took the subway down to Christopher Street. I wanted to check out the cock rings at the Christopher Street Bookstore. Franklin, the handsome Black guy, was at the counter dressed in his usual full leather. He's the owner. He knows me. He always turns me on. When he saw me staring at his crotch, he smiled and welcomed me into the shop. "How you doing Miles? I really like your motorcycle jacket. New? You look hot." Flattered, I told Franklin the jacket was indeed new and now I was looking for a new cock ring to go with it. "As you recall Franklin, I'm old-fashioned. I like the classic studded leather strap with adjustable snap buttons. Like what all the guys in Drummer wear." "Sure Miles, you have good taste. That's the model I use." Looking around, I sensed the store was empty. "Are you busy? Do you think maybe you could show me how it fits?" Of course, I had a hidden agenda. Franklin understood immediately. "Sure, the place is dead. Let me lock the front door for a few minutes." I leaned back against a glass display case, loosened my belt and fly and dropped my blue jeans. Franklin pulled my jock strap down. Then he took out the new cock ring and expertly positioned it nice and snug, not too tight, just perfect. "How's that feel? I'd say it's doing its job. You're already rock solid. Let me give you a hand with that." He then proceeded to jerk me off with a dab of lube from a hand dispenser on the countertop. He's a real pro. I guess he keeps the lube out for occasions like this.

Thursday March 4, 1982

Fourth therapy session with Terrence. I talked a lot. Terrence kept asking me questions, lots of them.

"Let's start with the "slut" question? I think you put it simply. 'Miles is a slut.' Is that correct?" I guess so. But I'm not really. I was totally 100% faithful to Jim for years, up until the end when we drifted apart.

42

"How did you feel as you experienced Jim drifting away from you?" Frightened. I didn't know what was happening. I felt out of control.

"When you were in Venice, did you feel different?" Yes, I felt strong and alive. I felt independent. I felt sexy. It was wonderful.

"Were you a slut in Venice?" No, not at all. It was beautiful. My lovers were magnificent. I adored them both. They were my brothers. We bonded. They desired me as much as I desired them. They made me feel my best.

"What about the three visits to the WSS? You had sex three times with the same stranger right? Were you a slut then?" I asked Jim before I went. He said I could go. He encouraged it. Yes, I felt like a slut there. The guy was sleazy. He was raunchy. But I liked that. He was super-hot, like Jim wasn't. I wanted to get filthy dirty with him. Maybe I wanted to be a slut because I wanted to free myself of Jim. When I asked the guy to fuck me hard during our last encounter, I wanted to disappear. Jim had taken a new lover, he had rejected me for a twinkie half his age, he humiliated me after nine years together. I wanted this Hispanic stud to fuck me until I vanished.

"Why would Jim encourage you going to the sauna?" I don't know. I guess he was trying to prepare me for the end of our relationship. He's smart. He understood it was ending. He never told me what he was thinking. Maybe this was his way of telling me it was over. 'Go to the baths. Fuck your brains out. I don't care. I don't need you any longer.'

"What did Jim say when you told him you were going to Venice alone? You'd always shared vacations together right?" Yes right. He seemed hurt, like I'd wounded him. But he agreed quickly. He gave me his permission.

"Did Jim break your trust by getting involved with a new lover when you were in Venice?" Well, yes, it's ugly, but I think so. Yes, he did. It's not like

I was secretly meeting someone in Venice. Jim told me once later that he thought I was meeting up in Venice with my friend Darko from SOM. I told him that was utter nonsense. Darko is just a work buddy. Jim's nuts. I think Jim was using my absence away in Venice to find a new lover that would allow him to break away from me. It's that simple. I was suffocating Jim. He jumped at the opportunity to escape when I was away in Venice.

"Good work Miles. Let's take a break."

"What about your date with Douglas? You called it a 'fuck date.' I think you said it was the best butt sex you've ever had. Douglas had sex with you in his sling, correct?" Actually, Douglas was the one who first called it a 'fuck date.' But yes, to everything. Douglas was the best. He's a leatherman; he's sexually experienced; he's confident and egoless; he's a skilled lover; plus, he's a real person: brilliant, funny, sensitive, caring. He's just the best. Problem is, he doesn't want a relationship. We're sex buddies. Period. He sees me as a younger guy who needs a friend at this point in his life. He enjoys our sex as much as I do, but I don't think Douglas needs me. He just enjoys my company at the moment.

"How does that make you feel? Slutty?" No, maybe yes, a bit. I want someone just like Douglas that also wants me, someone who actually needs me. Someone who loves me.

"Do you think you'll have sex with Douglas in the future?" Probably. He would like to. But it's not essential. We aren't lovers, just sex buddies. We'll always be close friends.

"So how are you feeling now Miles? Are you a slut?" I'm definitely a little slutty. But that's OK. I like that. I think that's part of who I am. I like to get down and dirty with a hot guy, with somebody special who's also into raunchy sex. I need to taste and smell my lovers. But there's more to it all. There's love and affection. I connect with these guys: Douglas, Andrei, the Venetian gondolier, the Catholic priest, the Hispanic stud from WSS. I will cherish the memory of each of these guys for as long as I live. The therapy session was over.

FRIDAY MARCH 5, 1982

I've really been pouring it on at the Apple. I work out every day for two hours; starting to show some serious muscles. Taking a protein drink to put on bulk. Working particularly hard on chest and abdominals. My goal is "six pack" abs. Very exciting. If I keep this up, I'll have a "gym bod" in a couple of months. My muscles ache, but it's a good pain. Getting rid of that damn sissy image.

SATURDAY MARCH 6, 1982

Back to the Saint. Jim, Sandy and I dance together. Sandy is an incredible dancer. He easily steals the whole dance floor. It feels good. Jim is radiant. We have a great time together clowning around. I've become Sandy's new friend.

Of course, I can't resist the sex balcony. It's busy. I met Robert. He gives me a great blowjob in the dim light. He's super-sweet. Afterwards we talk for hours in the member's lounge. He has his hands all over me. He can't stop smiling. He takes me back to his condo in the Village on Seventh Avenue. It's minimalist gorgeous, all white. Robert is loaded. He's as anal as I am, super clean and neat. He owns a design company that makes educational toys for children. Robert is too tired for sex, so I crash on his bed and sleep until two in the afternoon. When I come to, I start snooping around and I discover his neat-as-a-pin closet with a dozen white pressed Calvin Klein t-shirts and a dozen pairs of black pressed 501s. He gets my vote for best dressed fag. I'm feeling horny, but Robert says we have a dinner reservation for sushi in an hour. He wants to treat me. Lots of talk through dinner. He's very animated. Smiling at me all the time. He tells me about his beach house in Provincetown. He wants to take me there for a few days soon. But first he has a surprise. While I was asleep, he'd planned a quick trip to Washington D.C. for tomorrow. His treat. We'll be flying, staying the night in Georgetown at his favorite boutique hotel. Catch a couple museums.

It's all going so fast with Robert. He's obviously crazy about me for some unknown reason. We share a lot in common. Maybe he loves my big cock. That was a memorable blowjob at the Saint. But I noticed he never talks about sex. He never talks dirty, not even a little bit. In that way, he's like my mother Terry. We've hardly had any sex at all. I expected more. He's passive, a bottom. He likes to get butt-fucked, but he's really old school, a lot like Jim. Lights off. No foreplay. Nothing kinky. But I admit I love all the attention. Robert absolutely adores me. He's put me on a pedestal. That feels so good after Jim's recent neglect. We'll see where it goes from here.

MONDAY MARCH 7-8, 1982

Washington D.C. with Robert. We fly first class. Georgetown hotel is deluxe. Robert pays for everything. He takes me to Dumbarton Oaks, a Philip Johnson design. It's beautiful, a carpet of interlocking circles. Robert knew I'd like it. I'm impressed. He really tunes into my love of art and architecture. We spend the afternoon at the National Gallery of Art. I.M. Pei's addition is impressive. Robert shows me his favorite painting in the collection, a Turner seascape. I show him a favorite painting of mine, a homoerotic watercolor by John Singer Sargent of three dirty workmen in the stone quarry at Carrara, Italy. The difference does not go unnoticed.

On the flight back, I start feeling trapped. I'm suffocating under all this attention. Robert feels like a sugar daddy, maybe it's nice, but I don't think so. I'm torn. He's so perfect, so attentive and gentle, so filthy rich and comfortable. I've never come close to finding a partner like Robert. But I'm troubled. He's too clean, too proper. I miss Andrei's erotic passion. I miss the Hispanic stud's raunchy sex. I miss my hot gondolier and my cute Catholic priest. By the time I finally get home, back in my bed in my loft, I realize it's over. Robert is too much like Jim, too guarded, too closed, and definitely too uptight around sex. I need something more. It's over.

Tuesday March 9, 1982

I joined the Chelsea Gym today. Fantastic. I love it. It's the real thing; Chelsea's hot gay gym for sexy musclemen in skimpy spandex. I'm ready. I'll have my work cut out for me now. Free weights, of course. Guys helping each other out. Super-friendly. Plus, the steam room for a little action after a hard workout.

Wednesday March 10, 1982

I called up Robert. I proposed dinner out, this time my treat, at my favorite Cuban restaurant in the Village, Il Sabor, on Cornelia Street near his condo. Robert showed up on time in his usual pressed white t-shirt and black 501s. I told him our brief adventure was over. I thanked him for his love and generosity. I tried to explain the problem was me, not him. I explained I need more sex. I can't help myself. I crave sex, even dirty, even kinky sex, to be really happy, especially after years of living with Jim. He looked crushed. I felt awful. He shed a tear. I was a wreck, but we parted with a long warm hug. He blushed red as I reached down and gave his butt a nice firm squeeze right there in the middle of Cornelia Street. I told him I hoped we could remain friends.

Thursday March 11, 1982

Fifth therapy session with Terrence. He wanted to start with Jim. I talked and talked.

"How was your sex with Jim?" The first time I had sex with Jim it was in his cave-like basement apartment in total darkness. Not a word was spoken. Jim tried to butt-fuck me. It was a disaster; I was in total agony. I was a near virgin at the time, clueless. Jim's sex techniques back then were a bit clumsy and limited at best. So, of course he stopped and we traded positions. That arrangement was sort of satisfactory for both of us. For the next nine years it was always pretty much the same—Jim bottom, me top. No variety. At least I eventually got the lights on. It was a little boring. Predictable. Once a week I'd get to butt-fuck him. Never any oral sex from Jim. I always really missed that. But I enjoyed sucking him off. Any foreplay was always initiated by me. Jim never talked about sex. Period. He also never talked dirty during sex. I would have liked that. With Jim sex was mechanical, pretty joyless, rather sad really. And this went on for years. No sense of a shared adventure or fun. Pretty lousy.

"So, when you brought it up with Jim, what did he say?" Nothing, he'd make up some excuse and change the subject.

"How did sex with Robert compare to your sex with Jim?" Quite similar. I really tried my best to arouse Robert sexually in new fun exciting ways. He just wasn't interested. Totally passive. This concerned me from the start. Robert, much like Jim, was otherwise such a sensitive attractive partner, that I tried to play down the boring sex. I thought: "Maybe it will pick up." "Sex isn't everything right?" Wrong.

"You said you felt trapped with Robert. Can you explore that thought?" I think Robert would have provided me with everything I dreamed of. Like a sugar daddy. It came too easy. But I knew he would require total fidelity in exchange, like I had with Jim for years. I couldn't fuck around. He didn't come right out and say it, but I sensed it. He told me he wasn't interested in going back to the Saint, as if I might find someone else there to replace him.

"Would you look for sex outside the relationship with Robert, maybe even at the Saint?" Honestly, I think I would sooner or later, probably in leather bars, not the Saint. I couldn't stop myself. I crave a butch hot leatherman. That's just not who Robert is. If I moved in with Robert, I'd be out on the prowl looking for Mr. Right while wearing my new motorcycle jacket. I couldn't help myself. It would not be fair to Robert.

"Did Robert need you?" He only wanted me like a possession; like a painting you put on the wall. He didn't connect with my deeper side, my hidden erotic side. It's really a shame the way things worked out.

"Good work Miles. Next, I'd like you to talk about your attraction to leathermen. When did it start?" Back at Cornell when I saw Marlon Brando as the butch motorcycle guy in The Wild One. I loved him. He was tough. Later I saw real leathermen walking the streets of the West Village. I'd stare at them, their thick black moustaches, their work boots and chaps, their leather codpieces, their black leather motorcycle jackets. Couples walking boldly together with their hands locked tight on each other's butt, declaring their sexual preference with a colored bandana in the rear pocket for all to see. I thought they were the most beautiful men in the world.

"What's so wrong with being a sissy? Oscar Wilde was a sissy." I hate the label. It's for losers, guys they pick last in team sports, guys with no muscles, weaklings. A playground bully called me a 'sissy' in front of everyone. He humiliated me. But even worse Terry would say, 'Miles, don't be such a sissy.' That really hurt.

"So, you joined the Chelsea Gym this past week? Why?" I'm tired of being a sissy. I'm going to get muscles, a gym bod, so I can attract the leatherman of my dreams. The Chelsea is where all the hot butch guys work out. I've got my work cut out for me, but for the first time in years, I'm motivated.

"Will you go back to the Saint looking for Mr. Right in the sex balcony?" No, that chapter has closed. Anyway, I'm not a member and Jim and Sandy leave town by the end of July. Plus, it's not really me. I don't know who the new Miles is yet, but I don't think he's going to be a disco bunny.

I'm going to Providence, Rhode Island next weekend to visit my parents. It will be the first visit there without Jim in nearly nine years. I don't know what to expect. Everybody in my family loved Jim, so our breakup has been a shock for them too. Members of my family are a lot like Jim, they're private and silent about anything to do with sex. But I need a distraction. Just getting away from the city and all this self-indulgent sex for a few days sounds good to me.

Session is over.

Friday March 12, 1982

I'm headed to Providence on Amtrack early tomorrow morning for the weekend. My parents, sister and her husband will be there. We never talk much about ourselves in my family. Very private. We'll probably play Scrabble. See the current art show at the RISD Museum. A nice seafood dinner out overlooking the ocean somewhere. No one will bring up Jim, but he will always be just below the surface.

Late Friday afternoon, I'm sitting at my desk in SOM, bored. I've been thinking about the tearoom at the IRT #1 subway station for hours. I figure I'm not going to see any action in Providence for days, that's for sure, so I decide I'll hit the subway tearoom on my way home.

I was in my Brooks Brothers suit for work. Inside the men's room things were really hopping. I turned on instantly. I unzipped and pulled it out, leaving my belt and trousers on. Just hanging out there, it was pretty raunchy. It got noticed right away by this blond jogger who was dripping sweat. He took it in deep. He was just what I always dream of most, a cocksucker pro. I wished it could last forever. What an athlete. He was fantastic. When I finally popped, he took it all. He was a perfect 10.

Saturday March 13, 1982

In Providence everyone is acting as if somebody died. They were all comfortable seeing Jim and me together as the "happy gay monogamous couple." We were so respectable. Maybe Jim and I separating is for the best. It's just possible, right? But Catholics aren't like the rest of the human race. They stay glued together no matter what. Sometimes in miserable marriages for decades.

Everyone is being super nice to me, but we don't say much. Terry asks me if I need anything, which I don't. How's work? They ask about Venice which is a little awkward. I have a few blown glass Christmas tree ornaments for them which I brought back in my luggage. We have a very nice dinner out on the coast. Great fresh seafood.

Sunday March 14, 1982

Sunday morning, we all dress up for church. After being in all those gorgeous Renaissance Venetian churches I'm totally spoiled, a snob. Their church here is so plain vanilla. Plus, I keep thinking about my sex in the vestry with my horny Venetian priest. Compared to these tired old straight guys, he was a Chippendale Adonis, a porno star.

I'm starting to fully realize how different my life is from my family; especially since my slutty behavior in Venice. Living in gay Manhattan is like being on another planet. People in Providence don't hang out in dark backrooms having sex with strangers or even worse in subway tearooms, that's for sure. I'm especially awkward around my poor sick father who is fighting cancer. I can't share anything personal with him; none of the affection I feel for all other men. Sensing this, he must feel miserable around me. We barely exchange a word. He can't even look me in the eye. I can tell he feels awful inside. It's really sad. I don't know what to do.

My sister has an antique upright piano in her living room. I brought along some sheet music so I could play. I'm a little rusty, but nobody complains. They all love it. It reminds them of the Miles they knew as a young boy, before homosexuality took him away from them. The piano music fills up the whole house as they go about their various chores, even up into the attic where no one goes anymore. It fills the empty spaces between each of us. I play Chopin for hours. It's my gift to each of them.

Monday March 15, 1982

I'm behind at work. Overtime late. Bob was there as well. I was horny after Providence, but I needed to focus on work. No sex tonight.

Tuesday March 16, 1982

After work I stayed in and read. Lawrence Ferlinghetti, A Coney Island of the Mind. Terrific poetry. Especially poem #7, the hetero sex scene: "on that hot riverbank where ferns fell away in the broken air of the breath

51

of her lover and birds went mad and threw themselves from trees to taste still hot upon the ground the spilled sperm seed" Wow! What a powerful image!

WEDNESDAY MARCH 17, 1982

I simply couldn't help myself; I went back to the Stud directly after work. It's been almost a week since I had any sex. My heart was pounding as I walked through the front door; my boner was easy to spot in my tight chinos. On the way in I spotted a real leatherman posing at the bar in his motorcycle jacket, chaps and leather codpiece. He was right out of Tom of Finland. He saw me stop to check him out and then followed me into the backroom. "Boy, show me your pretty butt." He liked to play rough. He slapped my bare butt hard with his hand, each time making a loud sharp pop that turned me on. The burning sting felt good; just what I wanted. I heard him unsnap his leather cod piece, slip on a condom and mutter, "Ready Boy?" He quickly found his rhythm and let loose. I saw stars. I only wished the lights were on so I could have seen him better. Unfortunately, I'll never know who he was. He disappeared into the darkness.

THURSDAY MARCH 18, 1982

Sixth therapy session with Terrence. It's been a busy week. I have a lot to tell Terrence. He has some good questions.

"How do you feel about your trip last week to see your family?" It was alright, but I feel the distance between our lives. Especially with all my recent sex adventures. If they knew they'd be very disappointed in me.

"Why do you say that?" For them, all sex is shameful, even straight sex. Gay sex is unspeakable. They don't see the beauty in sex the way I do. They'd call me a slut for sure if they saw me carrying on. Why just last night I had tremendous anonymous sex at the Stud with my first butch leathermen. I couldn't possibly share that experience with my family. Yet it was a highpoint of my life.

"You said you had your first sexual encounter with a real leatherman last night in the backroom at the Stud correct? So, how was it? How did it meet your expectations? How did it make you feel?" It was intense, off the chart. While it was going on I felt tremendous. Later on, when I got home, it was not so great. It was all physical. I missed an emotional connection. It should have been obvious. It's hard to get to know someone in the dark right?

"Yes. Good insight. Was the physical side satisfying?" As it happened absolutely. Later on less so.

"So, you never spoke to the leatherman at the Stud?" Not really. These pitch-black backrooms are not conducive to building new relationships.

"So why do you keep going back?" I can't seem to help myself. I've had tremendous sex at the Stud. I'm a sex addict.

"I wouldn't get hung up on labels. Let's just say you really enjoy sex. Agreed?" Yes absolutely.

"You can choose to return to the Stud or not. It's your choice. Just own it." Yes, you're right. I'm ashamed. Forgive me. I'm out of control.

"That's not necessary, don't be hard on yourself Miles. You're in a safe space here. You should feel comfortable saying whatever you feel. Just be honest. And love yourself." I'll try harder.

"Thank you. Let's take a short break." I felt really shaken up. Terrence knew immediately. He gave me a long warm hug. I broke down crying. I slowly composed myself. Terrence continued:

"Let me be so bold as to summarize your present situation. If I am out of line please come after me. You've recently lost your beloved. Whether you drifted apart or he betrayed you or you betrayed him, it doesn't really matter. It's over. You are a widow. Suddenly you're a single gay man living alone in Manhattan. That's pretty scary. That's a tectonic shift for you. Give yourself time and space to adjust. Be gentle with yourself Miles. You're doing just fine. I'm proud of you. Let me give you another hug." I started crying again like a baby. Terrence held me as long as I needed. He was warm and wonderful.

But he's tough. Terrence jumped right in again.

"Let's talk about anonymous sex. You've seen plenty of that lately in tearooms, backrooms, saunas right? Can you talk about those encounters?" They were almost always super charged, illicit, extra hot at the time they occurred. When it was over, I was light headed and feeling marvelous each time. But it faded pretty quickly. In a few days the memory was fuzzy and another fresh encounter was needed to take its place. One led to the next. Nothing like my sex with Douglas. Those encounters remain vivid for many weeks, and with a few, like my sling sex with Douglas, it can last forever. It's because they were about more than just sex. We shared emotions, affection, even love. Great sex yes, but something more lasting. I crave that connection.

"Sounds like you prefer sex with someone you know, or at least want to know. Someone you respect." Yes, that's absolutely true. Like with Douglas, he has a brilliant mind. I can learn so much from him. He's not just a hot butch leatherman, but he's also a deep, intelligent, caring, sensitive man. I definitely respect Douglas.

"I sense you aren't much of a cheater, once you commit yourself to someone. Is that true? Put Venice aside a moment. It was outside your real life, like in a dream." Neither Jim or I ever cheated on each other. If I really love someone completely, as I did with Jim for nine years, I would never cheat on him. It's like when I told you last week, I couldn't pretend to be in a committed relationship with Robert, while secretly having sex with some butch leatherman. What I want and need is a serious committed loving relationship with a spectacular man, who happens to be butch, hot and into leather.

'So, tell me again. What is Miles looking for?" Yes, that's it. It's so obvious. I'm looking for a hot butch leatherman, the Marlboro Man without the cigarette. He's handsome, confident, masculine, well-endowed. He's into leather, but not the whip and chains. He loves sex, clean or dirty, top or bottom, anytime, anywhere. Inside he's a mushy romantic like me, fiercely devoted and faithful, intelligent, kind, caring, generous, egoless, patient and empathetic. He'd demand total monogamy, which I could gladly give him. We'd even share outside sex adventures as long as we were both completely on board.

"Good work Miles. This week I want you to focus on your Marlboro Man. Visualize him in detail. Get a strong mental picture of him. Do some play acting. Make him human, more than a sex stud. Talk to him. Tell him a dirty joke. Make him laugh. Make him do the same for you. Have fun. Can you do that for me Miles?" I'll try my best Terrence. This week's goodbye hug felt especially good.

Friday March 19, 1982

A new Miles. We'll see how far I get. It feels like an uphill climb. Even though it's a red-hot Friday night, I decided to stay in and do some reading. I started Dicken's Bleak House before Venice and of course got totally distracted when I returned. Jim always pushed Dickens on me. It was fine, I ended up loving his characters. Time to check in on Esther Summerson. After reading for two hours non-stop, I had enough for the evening. I pulled out a few favorite issues of Drummer, always my first choice for J.O. material. It's all about leather sex. The new Miles definitely has some old habits.

Saturday March 20, 1982

I headed out early to Canal Street. I'm going to the art supply store. I have always wanted to try my hand at oil painting. This is as good a time as any, that's for sure. A small easel, brushes, tubes of oil paint, assorted tools. Small canvas boards to start with. I decided to try painting an apple for starters, seated at a huge loft window. I chose a red Macintosh. What's nice with oil paint is it takes days to dry, so you can play with it. The board for the apple is only 6"x 8". The apple fills up half the canvas. Looks surprisingly realistic.

The cherry trees in City Hall Park are starting to open with gorgeous fleshy pink blossoms. I love them. That's going to be my next subject. I'll set up my easel in the park. A little larger for sure. Loose, painterly, like the French Impressionists. I'm having fun.

2

Spring

Sunday March 21, 1982

It's the first day of spring. How apropos that I'm painting flowers. What a coincidence.

I haven't gotten very far with my homework assignment for Terrence—visualizing my dream Marlboro Man. He suggested role playing. That's easy. I already do that. I can easily find my guy in the pages of Drummer. He's easily cloned. I can imagine all kinds of situations with my guy, both clean and dirty. He's butch gorgeous, with a warm open smile, always up for sex, well-endowed of course, but a pussy cat inside. We enjoy every kind of sex in the book. He makes me laugh a lot. We're best friends. We never argue about anything. We share everything. I tell him my most private dirty secret and he hugs me like it's nothing. He's spectacular. But where can I find this amazing man?

Monday March 22, 1982

I finished Bleak House. It's great. Next, I'm going to read Christopher Isherwood's A Single Man. I thought it would be apropos to my current state. Plus, I want to read an openly gay author right now. I need my own community right now.

TUESDAY MARCH 23, 1982

I went to the Frick today by myself. I haven't been in a quality museum, other than RISD, since I left Venice. Jim and I loved the Frick. It was our favorite New York City museum. Not too big, intimate. And paintings of the highest quality: Vermeers, Carots and Sargents, even a whole room of Fragonards. Ah, the two passionate straight lovers in the garden, he's kneeling with his hand buried in her lap. What comes next?

While salivating over a Carot, I heard from behind, "Well hello stranger." It was Richard. I hadn't seen him since our Cornell graduation picnic eight years ago. He looked great. He introduced me to his 'partner' Gerald. They were both glowing. Richard actually looked hot. He was even showing some muscles. That was a new development. When we did our urban design thesis together, he was always so effete, a bit too formal. Richard asked about Jim. He and Jim got along well. When I told him we had broken up after nine years together, he was stunned. He told me he'd always admired us as positive gay role models. Little does he know.

We had lunch in the museum café. I decided to ask him the question I had been holding onto all these years. "At Cornell, were you a secret cross dresser?" He turned beet red. "Yes, how did you know that?" I explained that whenever I picked him up at his Collegetown apartment building at the top of Buffalo Street, he took at least twenty minutes to appear. Plus, he never invited me in. I figured he's so private he must be hiding something. Turns out, I was right. When we parted I gave his cute bubble butt a friendly squeeze. "So that's how it feels after all these years of just looking. Very nice Richard."

WEDNESDAY MARCH 24, 1982

I picked up the latest Cadinot porno flick from the Christopher Street Bookshop, Aime…Comme Minet. It stars the incredibly sexy Pierre Buisson in an erotic photo shoot with Cadinot himself behind the camera. What a dick on this kid. He cuts to two sex scenes – one in a bread bakery, the other with a jogger in a Parisian park. God it's beautiful. Rather than carrying on like a slut in places like the Stud, maybe staying in and watching some quality porn is a healthier substitute. The second feature is a sweet flick about phone sex and poolside sex. Cadinot's always the best. The young guys are so cute and well-hung. Maybe my image of the perfect Marlboro Man is too dark, too butch. Cadinot's boys are usually super-sweet, horny yes, but really nice wholesome guys, lots of cute smiles, the type my Mom would drool over.

THURSDAY MARCH 25, 1982

My seventh therapy session with Terrence. It was a good one.

"So, you've been busy. I understand your past week has been a little different. How do you feel?" More in control. More like my old life I experienced with Jim. Except I'm alone. I'm often lonely. New projects like painting, reading and my trip to the Frick have been good distractions while they lasted. But I always end up alone in bed, jerking off to Drummer or a Cadinot porno flick. This monastic life can only last so long. Eventually I'm going to have to face the fact that I need to meet new people, play the dating game, circulate somehow. I'm not sure where to begin. Finding Mr. Right feels like climbing Mount Everest.

"How did your visualization exercises go?" I felt a little silly frankly. I'd rather spend the time talking to a real person.

"That's fine. Are you ready?" Maybe. I'd like to try. But I need to find the right person to approach. I can't just walk up to anyone, can I?

"Why not? If it feels right, jump in, say hello. Show an interest in the other person. Have fun. Show them that beautiful smile of yours. You're a very desirable guy. Don't focus on sex. That will take care of itself in due time." Really, you think so? You make it sound so easy.

"Miles, you're a catch. I'm telling you honestly as another gay man. So, relax. Enjoy the guys all around you. Smile, maybe say hello to a cute stranger on the street if it feels right. Try cruising in the afternoon daylight as well as 2 o'clock in the morning in a backroom. Make your search for your next beloved fun." You're right Terrence. I never fully realized that I'm looking for my beloved, the most wonderful man in the world. That sounds a little different from looking for a good butt-fuck, if you know what I mean?

"Well said." Sounds kind of fun. More like play than some hot sex game where I have to perform. But where do I start?

"Perhaps you should look where you least expect it. You're painting right? Well maybe you join a painting class at New York University, right here in the Village. The cute guy at the easel standing next to you might return your smile. Or say you're going to the Metropolitan Museum of Art. I know you're very interested in art right? So, when you go, don't walk around all by yourself; take the full length, extra-long docent tour. You might find Mr. Right standing next to you. Maybe he's the hot one leading the tour. Maybe you meet an interesting gay couple on the tour. Well, they may be just the ones to match you up with Mr. Right. Just relax. Be open to all opportunities. That doesn't rule out your favorite leather bar, backroom or sauna late at night. All us gay guys need some of that action too. Just remember in hot situations involving speechless anonymous sex, the guy you want to fuck is a person just like you, someone you could potentially share your whole life with. He could be more than just the perfect fuck buddy; he could be your future beloved. Treat him with love and respect." I started crying. Terrence gave me one of his warm wonderful hugs. I'm so lucky to have him as my therapist, as a friend.

FRIDAY MARCH 26, 1982

This morning I looked into oil painting classes at New York University. They offer an eight-week beginner's class that starts soon in early April. It's taught by a guy named Daniel. He's supposed to be great. It's limited to ten students. Sounds perfect. I'm excited!

Saturday March 27, 1982

Simon from work called up. He knows I'm really lonely so he proposed a tour tonight of the Mine Shaft. Simon is a member; it's a sex club. I've never been. I've always been curious. Terrence is bound to be disappointed with me. I told Simon I'll meet him there at midnight.

The Mine Shaft is located in the Meat Packing District in the middle of nowhere. It's a little scary. I met Simon out front on Washington Street near Little West 12th A steady stream of super-butch leatherman were showing up in cabs. I took one look at these guys and I knew I was in the wrong place. They looked mean. What was I thinking? Simon is all jacked up, eager to give me the full tour. I feel trapped. Nervous, I resigned myself to going inside.

Of course, it's world famous for its debauchery. First thing I noticed, it's grimy and there was no sign. Just the street number 835 on a red metal door. Inside a bouncer screened out guys who didn't meet their strict dress code which only permits biker leather, Levi's, jock straps and uniforms. No cologne, suits, ties, disco drag and no sneakers. I checked my leather motorcycle jacket and t-shirt. I decided to hold on to my ratty old Levi's, although many of the patrons were buck naked. Afterall, it is a sex club. Simon went bare except for his black leather chaps. He fit right in.

The club was on two levels. First floor was for the more hardcore super-butch types. It was called the "Playground" with a jail cell, the back of a truck and dungeons. Up the narrow flight of stairs to the second floor was a bar. Nearby was a roof deck. After giving me the tour, Simon headed back down to the first floor. I felt more comfortable on level two at the bar, watching guys going at it. It was a sight. I thought of Terrence. I'm not sure how he'd suggest I approach any of these guys in conversation about anything other than sex.

A butch older guy with a bald head and a bushy black mustache appeared out of nowhere. "Hey kid, can I buy you a beer? I'm Jack." "Hi, I'm Miles.

Thanks. I'm drinking Pellegrino. My first time here. Pretty wild." "It's all an act, most of these guys are sissies." "Somehow I doubt that. You certainly look butch, like those guys in Drummer." Jack was bare chested, dressed in just old leather chaps over ripped Levi's. He was carrying a leather paddle. "Miles, could I interest you in some sling sex?" "I'll take a rain check. No offence, but you're old enough to be my father. I'm not looking for a sugar daddy." "I hear you kid. But don't disrespect your elders." We both shared a good laugh. I liked Jack immediately.

Jack and I talked for hours on the roof deck in our motorcycle jackets. When Simon finally showed up at 3 am, I was ready to catch a cab home. Jack handed me his card. "Kid, it's been nice talking to you. Most guys here never say a word. Give me a call. I'm at One Christopher Street. I even know how to cook." We chuckled again. I really enjoyed meeting Jack. He made the Mine Shaft human.

SUNDAY MARCH 28, 1982

I ran into Michael leaving the Chelsea Gym on 17th Street. I hadn't seen him in years. He was my old boss at his small architectural firm on Canal Street. I recalled how he was always putting the make on me in the office. He must have seen me always staring at his sexy butt. Back then I was naïve and super-shy. I was afraid to take him up on his seductive glances. What a huge mistake. He was looking great today, all pumped up from his workout, even butcher than I remembered. I decided to give him a shot. "Hey Michael. You look great! How have you been?" "I've been well. Staying busy. Today's my day off. I heard you and Jim broke up. Need a little distraction?" "Sure. What did you have in mind?" "How about a long hot shower back at my apartment?" "Sounds great buddy. I'd like to suds up that gorgeous butt of yours. You know I've had my eye on it for years."

MONDAY MARCH 29, 1982

Back in the office early Monday morning, I told Bob all about my Sunday hookup with Michael. He was jealous.

TUESDAY MARCH 30, 1982

Still horny from the weekend, I started thinking about Wolf, the Black stud I met a couple of weeks ago in the Wall Street Sauna. I still had his business card in the box on my desk. I had never used it. I really liked Wolf. I fondly recalled his huge Black cock and our amazing sex. I called him up. "Hey Wolf. This is Miles from the WSS. Remember the white guy you fucked in the steam room on a snowy night? Could I interest you in another round? So you remember? Cool. Oh really? Great! Sure, I can be there in twenty minutes tops. I'll be in the steam room waiting for you. That's right, I miss you too. Look for a yellow jock strap."

WEDNESDAY, MARCH 31, 1982

I'm flying like a kite. Last night's sex with Wolf was fantastic. He called me at work to tell me he had a really good time. He wants me to meet his roommate Timmy on Friday at his apartment. Timmy is majoring in poetry at New York University. He's from California, a sexy beach bum with blond hair. A queer hippie. Wolf told me Timmy has read all my poetry books and is a big fan. Timmy is a young queer poet himself and wants to show me some of his new poems. Wolf thinks Timmy would also like to fool around. I'd really enjoy that. The new generation of queer poets are so refreshing. They are all so liberated. I love their work.

Maybe this sex thing could include some poetry readings. Could be a really cool juxtaposition. Mix up reading poetry with live queer sex. Bob, Billy and Douglas would certainly be interested. Maybe we could call it: Sex & Poetry. Seems crazy, but why not? Sort of like the Greenwich Village beatnik coffee house scene of the 50s, but not smokey. Way better than the subway tearooms. Wolf was on board 100%. He'll invite Timmy. I'll have to tell Terrence all about this idea tomorrow.

THURSDAY APRIL 1, 1982

My eighth therapy session with Terrence. I have so much to talk about.

Terrence starts with something else. 'Miles, I'm glad to hear you're starting an oil painting class at New York University. I've always heard good things about their programs." Yes, I'm looking forward to my first class on April 6th.

"Now, let's get down to the big news this week. You went to the Mine Shaft, right? How was that?" Not what I expected. The place is raunchy. I met a butch older guy named Jack. We talked for hours. No sex. I really like him. I like his sense of humor. A new friend. Jack humanized the Mine Shaft.

"Congratulations Miles, I think you handled the Mine Shaft very well."

I wanted to tell Terrence about my run in with my ex-boss Michael. It was payoff from secret lusts we both formed years ago. We had fantastic shower sex. Just goes to show you the power of sex. A hardon can last for decades. "Miles, you're absolutely right. Congratulations!"

I told Terrence about my planned Sex & Poetry session for tomorrow night with Wolf and Timmy. The idea is to see if we can combine live sex with a poetry reading. Timmy and I write queer love poems. We want to share them with other gay men during group sex.

"Sounds fascinating and very hot. By the way Miles, I've read your love poetry; it's really sexy. Good luck tomorrow. Play safe."

FRIDAY APRIL 2, 1982

Timmy, Wolf and I had our "test" session of Sex & Poetry on pillows in their apartment. I was treated as the guest of honor. We first stripped naked with me standing in the middle. Since Timmy is strictly into oral sex and Wolf is strictly into anal sex, it made sense for them to work as a team servicing me separately, front for Timmy, rear for Wolf. What an honor. I read my homoerotic poem "A Lad's Rump" from my poetry book Labyrinth. Six four-line stanzas. I must say, I've never enjoyed such outrageous sex. Timmy blew me as only he knows how and Wolf butt-fucked me straight to heaven, both at the same time, while I stood reading the erotic poem with exaggerated expression. They both discovered that the words of poetry added to their sexual performance.

A faceless lad poses in a doorway,
his pale rump is round and fine.
He rubs it with his free hand,
he knows he makes me pine.

His butt crack is so erotic,
the cheeks so soft and full.
My gaze remains unbroken,
I'm raging like a bull.

I slap his pink cheeks firmly,
it sounds sharp like a gun.
I use my bare raw hands,
I'm having more than fun.

Who is this faceless angel?
His stance so debonair.
I can only see his buttocks,
a hint of his blond hair.

I finger his deep butt crack,
I rim his silky anus.
I fuck him in the doorway,
I'm sure that will sustain us.

My cock slides deep inside him,
I give him my warm cum.
He remains my faceless angel,
I can hear the ancient drum.

We all spilled our seed and rested in each other's arms. Timmy read love poems full of lust and longing—raw and honest. I read another poem from my book XXX Love Poems, full of homoerotic sex taboos and off-color humor. The sexually charged poetry kept us aroused. It went like that all evening, queer poetry followed by even queerer sex. One fed the other. We all agreed the first meeting of Sex & Poetry was a great success. We planned an expanded version in two weeks. I will invite Bob, Billy and Douglas to join us.

SATURDAY APRIL 3, 1982

My first oil painting class at New York University is only three days away. It's in their adult continuing ed program. I'm sure to be one of the oldest students in the class. It should be fun being surrounded by twenty-year-old's.

I decided to practice painting outdoors in City Hall Park. The weather is glorious. The pink blossoms on the cherry trees are peeking. Petals carpet the ground. I setup my easel just at the edge of the pink sea of petals. I want to paint just the petals out of context, a hint of green grass showing through. My challenge is to capture the delicate texture of the individual petals, to bring them to life. I discovered the trick is to paint loosely, with my eyes half closed in a trance. Get lost in the sea of petals falling out of the cobalt blue sky. I paint four versions, all two-foot squares. The first two are much too tight. Next I used a much broader brush over an orange undercoat applied with a rag and linseed oil. Much better! It has come to life. The last canvas used a turquoise undercoat with similar pink petals. It was interesting, but it lacked the luminosity of number three. A self-proclaimed art critic walking past said I forgot to include the tree trunks. "Maybe next time. Thanks for the tip."

SUNDAY APRIL 4, 1982

My gay boss Stanley at SOM gave me an extra pair of tickets to Harvey Fierstein's Broadway play Torch Song Trilogy. I was touched. Stanley had met Jim at the SOM Christmas party last year at Tavern on the Green and really liked him. Jim could be a real charmer. I told Stanley about our breakup. Stanley encouraged me to invite Jim and see the play with him. "Miles, it's important to stay in touch with your old lovers. I learned that lesson the hard way. I lost many dear friendships foolishly. These men are your family."

Of course, Jim accepted and personally thanked Stanley. Afterwards Jim took me out to our old favorite Broadway restaurant, Tout va Bien. Just the two of us. The restaurant was exactly the same. The French food was still first rate. It felt strange being there with Jim, like in a time warp. The play was outstanding. Jim enjoyed it. When we finally parted to go our separate ways, I felt light-headed. Back home, alone in my loft, I thought back on Jim and our nine years of living together. I vowed to myself, that whatever else happens, I would stay in touch with Jim forever.

MONDAY APRIL 5, 1982

After work I made a run down to the art supply store on Canal Street to buy supplies for my painting class which starts tomorrow evening. The instructor is a guy named Daniel. I heard through my grapevine that Daniel is gay. Apparently he and Douglas had a one-night stand several years ago. Douglas said he was a good instructor. No ego and cute.

TUESDAY APRIL 6, 1982

My first oil painting class at New York University. I agree the cute instructor Daniel is obviously gay. He smiles and checks me out on my way in. I'm wearing my old tattered Levi cutoffs that will still be perfectly fine with a few paint smears added in. Daniel takes note of the cutoffs and gives me a thumbs up. I've brought along my painting supplies. As I'm settling in I hear a familiar voice from the back of the room. It's Timmy! What a pleasant surprise. We hug in the middle of the room in front of everyone. He's very cool and relaxed. Timmy explains. "I'm taking this course to meet an art distribution requirement. I'm not in Fine Arts. As you know Miles, I'm a poet." Daniel asks Timmy to take the empty seat next to me. His gaydar tells him that Timmy and I are already well acquainted.

67

For the first hour, Daniel has us draw a nude male model, probably a student looking to earn a few dollars. The model is trim and athletic, posing seated on a stool with his muscular legs wide open. Drawing his gorgeous cock is the biggest challenge. This must have been Daniel's idea, his way of welcoming the gay guys into his class. The second hour Daniel asks us to quickly paint the same model using oil paints. He urges us to paint expressively using our whole bodies, to be spontaneous and open, to take risks. Daniel is a great instructor.

As class winds down, I notice Timmy is hovering around me. Stepping close to my ear, he whispers almost inaudibly, "I had a ball last Friday at our little orgy." I ignored Timmy's hint for more sex and tried to change the subject. "Why don't you come downtown to my loft some day after class and we can make some poetry together. A real collaboration. Would you be interested? I know you graduate New York University in a few months right? I understand from Wolf that you're off to San Francisco." "That's right, I have a job lined up at City Lights Booksellers with Lawrence Ferlinghetti my hero." "Wow Timmy! I'm impressed."

WEDNESDAY APRIL 7, 1982

I woke up early thinking about Tim. He seems to be obsessed with me. He's a terrific cocksucker. But Tim is barely twenty-one. I'm almost ten years older. I shouldn't be fooling around with such a young guy. But he's leaving New York in a few months. Maybe we can have some harmless fun. I'm glad I'm seeing Terrence tomorrow. I need some outside perspective.

THURSDAY APRIL 8, 1982

It's my ninth therapy session with Terrence.

"Miles, I'd like to explore that men's shower room in your childhood. It was at a pool club back in Albuquerque right? How old were you?" Just ten.

"You just watched right?" Mostly. I'd watch the young guys suds up with soap, getting their swollen cocks all slippery with the white suds. Some guys would play with themselves. I wanted to touch them, but I knew I shouldn't.

"Did anything else happen?" Yes, once a beautiful middle-aged guy approached me; we were all alone. He just stood in front of me, covered in soap, completely still. He called me over, 'Look at this boy.' He let me touch his soapy cock with both hands. I wanted to. He didn't force me. It was beautiful. 'Go ahead boy. You can squeeze it.' It was hard. I rubbed the head with both hands. It felt rubbery. He started moaning softly. Then he started jerking himself off. I just stood there under the warm stream of water, gently holding his soapy soft balls in my cupped pair of hands. His warm cum splattered on my bare feet as he moaned looking up to heaven. 'Thanks kid. You're a good boy." He just walked away. I never saw him again.

"How did that episode leave you?" I felt special, like I had been chosen. Of course, I told no one. He was like a father. It was my secret to treasure forever. From that day forward I'd jerk off in private every day. I was in awe of my dick; I knew my cock was bigger than most in the showers.

"How do you feel about having a large cock?" I feel blessed, special. I know it's a little large, not enormous like most Black dicks. Of course, I had nothing to do with it. I never brag about it. I figure I'm just lucky. Like I won the lottery. It's God's gift.

"Now tell me about your sex with Tim." I met Tim a week ago at Wolf's threesome. Tim is a skilled cocksucker. He's really into my dick, just because it's big. He really knows how to give me pleasure. We both like to play a little slutty. I call him my Mr. Deep Throat.

"Yes, I can imagine. We know you like to play a little slutty right?" I guess so. Yes, I do. I can't help myself. But I promise to look after Tim. He's just a kid. I love him like a baby brother. But he's actually a full-grown young man. It's a little complicated.

"Sure, I understand Miles. Tim is like gay candy. Stay focused. Tim graduates soon. Maybe you can use this special friendship with Tim to address your larger issues surrounding casual sex. Remember you are still looking for your new beloved right? I think you realize Tim is not the one. Stay focused."

"Miles, let me summarize. You are in a difficult place. You've lost your center. For nine years Jim was your center. With his departure you are adrift in an ocean of emotions and desires. That's a lot to sort through. Give yourself time and space. Each week I note your progress. You have shown courage and love. You may not see it, but it's real. Hang in there buddy. Things will get easier, I promise."

FRIDAY APRIL 9, 1982

Tonight was supposed to be the party I arranged over a week ago with Douglas, Bob and myself. I felt awkward. They don't even know about Tim or Wolf. I decided it was the perfect time to bring up Sex & Poetry. Get feedback from everyone. Douglas really loved the whole idea from the get-go. Bob was on the fence, but I knew he'd come around. I told them I wanted to invite Billy as well. He could use some new friends. That would make six guys total counting Timmy and Wolf. Douglas offered to host it at his loft. He has a huge collection of poetry books. Plus he has a sex sling.

We decided to call off tonight's sex orgy and instead go for dinner in Chinatown. Douglas wants to treat. We targeted Saturday April 17th for the next enlarged session of Sex & Poetry. We all agreed to call meetings "Sessions" rather than "Orgies." The only ground rule would be everyone would read aloud from a poem they really loved. They could recite as many as they liked, at any time during any sex act. The idea was to mix up poetry and group sex, a new art form, join poetry and sex into one creative act, physical and cerebral. A new way to express ourselves.

70

SATURDAY APRIL 10, 1982

Tim asked me to find a way to get us into the Saint. I still had Andrei's card in my box. I called him up and he remembered our balcony sex vividly. He said sure, no problem, Tim and I could be his guests. I was nervous Andrei would expect me to have sex with him in exchange, but he was really nice about it. Hands off. He wished us a good time. I was impressed. It just goes to show you, all kinds of guys go to the Saint.

Tim had a ball. He went nuts on the dance floor, working up a sweat, dancing with strangers. He insisted we blow each other in the balcony. We closed the place and had a pancake breakfast afterwards on Second Avenue. I really had fun with Tim. He's so innocent and care free. He has a beautiful soul.

SUNDAY APRIL 11, 1982

I was lying in bed alone replaying in my head the sex scene with Wolf from last winter in the Wall Street Sauna. I could still recall it vividly. That was when we met. He was a wonderful lover. He's strictly a top. Wolf is into white ass.

I want to do something special for Wolf. He's been a little withdrawn lately. I have been preoccupied with Tim. I suggested to Wolf dinner at Café de la Gare. My treat. Wolf told me his life story over dinner. He grew up in Chicago, an only child. He's 25. His father was an engineer who died of a massive heart attack when Wolf was just nine years old.

Wolf is a New York University grad student majoring in business administration. He might work on Wall Street after graduation and try to get super rich as fast as possible. Wolf is also a serious body builder. He sometimes dreams of opening a free-weights gym in Chelsea. Maybe include a small café.

It's funny how different he is from Tim, the flower child hippie. Wolf and Tim aren't lovers, just best friends. Wolf's never been in a long-term relationship. Timmy comes the closest. He's afraid of growing old all alone. Wolf is a quiet, gentle giant. He rarely complains about anything.

MONDAY APRIL 12, 1982

Helmut called me up at work. He's the German stud from my past. Remember, we had two back-to-back sex scenes in the Bloomingdale's IRT tearoom last winter? He suggested we take along lunch break today and pop into the Metropolitan Museum of Art to look at their collection of ancient Greek and Roman statues. Helmut loves them. They are all so butch. The gallery is just off the main entrance. It has a coffered barrel-vaulted ceiling. The white marble statues on pedestals depict life-size male nudes: lovers, athletes, fighters, emperors, and gods. Helmut's favorite was a huge sarcophagus, with sides covered in carved stone relief, depicting a crowded maze of nude male figures, in a chaotic celebration of a military victory by Dionysus. It looked just like an orgy scene of Village boys, on a busy night at the Stud, with its interlocking limbs and torsos. Some things never change.

Afterwards, I thanked Helmut and gave him a warm hug. "Thanks buddy, I feel closer to you now." Helmut must be at least sixty-five, in great shape, with a sexy bald head. He's always hot in his leather chaps with his gorgeous sapphire blue eyes. I really love Helmut. He's the real thing. A stand-in Greek or Roman stud, nude with one of those hot bubble butts on display. That's Helmut, Mr. No Bullshit.

TUESDAY APRIL 13, 1982

I painted all morning in class. I've graduated to 24"x 30" stretched canvases. I'm doing a series of abstract horizontal landscapes. Taking risks with the edges between the colors. Trying to stay loose. It's a challenge. Doesn't always work, but a couple are quite decent. I wish I had the setup to do really large canvases, but that's not in the cards. I'm just a "weekend" painter, a dilettante. I enjoy it, but it lacks the emotional intensity of a Mark Rothko or a Helen Frankenthaler. Those folks are the real painters.

WEDNESDAY APRIL 14, 1982

When Jim left so suddenly the day I got back from Venice, he left behind the dozen postcards I sent him. They're still on the cookbook shelf above the washer and dryer. No one pays them any mind. There's the front of Santa Maria dei Miracoli where I met my gondolier. He has long forgotten me by now for sure. Venice seems like another universe to me now. So does Jim. He was the center of my world for nine years. I still cherish the quiet domestic life we shared together. I should call him up and see how he's doing.

All that happened well before the nonstop sex in the Saint, the backroom at the Stud, the sauna at the Chelsea Gym. Before butch Helmut and Wolf. Before sweet Timmy and Douglas. Before raunchy Mr. Jock Strap and Andrei at the Saint. I've been longing for my next beloved, my next center, ever since Jim departed. Terrence cautions I'm looking in all the wrong places. He's probably right. But where do I go next?

Robert would have given me anything I wanted. I pushed him away. Helmut was wise. He knew how to keep me happy. I teased him like a child. I forgot to show him my love. I wouldn't give poor Jack half a chance. He deserved better than that. I had good times with all of them, especially cute Tim. I really thought I loved each one. But in the end, I misjudged them all. I sold them short. They were each spectacular in their own way. I was blind. I ask for their forgiveness now, but it's too late.

Thus I go to sleep alone each night, my heart broken, my head full of anxiety. I wake up alone, in a panic, crying in the dark. I'm a curse to myself. I'm too controlling, too needy, too demanding. I drive kind guys away who are only searching for love themselves.

Thursday April 15, 1982

This was my tenth therapy session with Terrence. I was nervous about seeing him tonight. I was actually dreading it. I felt like I was letting Terrence down. I understood for the first time that my search to replace Jim was a failure. It was all just meaningless sex. My admitting that to Terrence would make it final. It felt like an enormous failure. I didn't want to share this failure with Terrence, but I knew I must.

"What's wrong Miles? You look upset. Come here. Please let me hold you. There, there. Cry, let it all out. You are in pain. Let it all out. Tears are good. Don't be so hard on yourself. Whatever it is, we will face it together." Please forgive me. Ask them all to forgive me. Jack and Robert. Helmut and dear Tim. I collapsed on Terrence's sofa.

I awoke at 4 am in the morning. I was on Terrence's sofa. There was no sign of Terrence. I was covered by a blanket. I read a note on the table with a telephone number and cab fare.

I decided to walk home alone as the deserted city slowly came to life. The lights were gorgeous. The garbage trucks whined in the distance. The sky slowly turned coral and pale blue. It reminded me of Venice; I smiled. The heavens were beautiful. I told myself to remember this sky tonight when I'm alone in the darkness. God was going to give me a second chance.

Friday April 16, 1982

I realized I had never grieved properly for Jim and me. The sudden end of our long relationship. I completely overlooked that. We all did. My parents and siblings, my sex buddies, my colleagues in the office. We should have had a huge mock funeral in a beautiful old cemetery with ancient trees, green grass and rolling hills. Lots of tears, hugs and funny stories to share. It would have felt more like an outdoor party than a funeral. Jim would be dancing barefoot in the grass. I can hear Dusty Springfield and the Moody Blues. They sooth my battered heart.

SATURDAY APRIL 17, 1982

Tonight was the big night, the kickoff session for Sex & Poetry. We all loved poetry and sex; this was our first attempt to join the two. Besides me, the session included Douglas and Bob, Billy and Wolf, plus Tim. I asked guys to wear anything that turns them on. I picked my yellow BIKE jock strap. Billy likes to play my twin, so he went with the same look in pink. Douglas feels sexiest as a butch bad ass, so he wore black leather chaps and nothing else. Bob came naked with just a black leather snap on cock ring. Wolf and Tim came dressed as the Devil and the Angel, in black and white jock straps with black and white leather harnesses.

We followed the setup from our earlier test. Thankfully my poem Confession turned us all on. If the reader wanted to modify the poem and make it raunchier that was fine. Just let the poetry inspire your sex. Once we finished the first cycle we all got the hang of it and it went smoothly. We had a ball. It was organic.

As a cute baby boy,
they preferred my backside.
The plump round fleshy butt,
they mistook me for a jock.
They all had to touch them,
give the cheeks a little pat.
When puberty arrived,
I was glad I had a cock.

I discovered my first hardon,
horsing around the pool shower.
I was always super horny,
  jerking-off with wads of spit.
It wasn't long before I learned,
my cock was my best friend.
I packed six inches hard,

inside my pants, it never fit.
I was always up for sex,
I always craved adventure.
I tried out boxer shorts,
jockstraps were always better.
I started off a top,
I ended up a bottom.
I never wore a dress,
I always worshipped leather.

I'm a Kinsey number six,
it never was a question.
I was born to suck a cock,
especially an erection.
Loneliness really sucks,
I always craved affection.
Sex is over rated,
true love is an illusion.

Chaps are really queer,
especially over Levi's.
An old jockstrap works best,
when I go out cruising.
I prefer my lovers butch,
with a touch of S&M.
A spanking with a paddle,
is always worth the bruising.

A guy's butt-crack is hot,
it always leaves me turned-on.
Black cock is often huge,
it's always good for screwing.
Italian men are sexy,
they never keep you waiting.
They're all so super cute,
especially when they're praying.

Things got pretty creative towards the end. Out came some sex toys to spice things up. The poem itself turned raunchy, word by word. It spun out of control as we all started laughing. But we all had a ball with sex and poetry.

SUNDAY APRIL 18, 1982

Jack invited me over for dinner at his place in One Christopher Street. He has a great apartment on a high floor with views. Jack lives alone. If he were closer to my age, I might well be all over him. He's very sexy for a sixty-five-year-old. He's even a great cook. He served Chinese Szechuan stir fry.

Jack confided he's tired of the Mine Shaft. He's getting too old. He's into Black dick up the ass. It seems he can't ever get enough. I immediately thought of Wolf's dick. I gave him Wolf's number. They could make a great butch couple. Jack thanked me profusely. He's lonely like me.

MONDAY APRIL 19, 1982

After an early supper, I headed to Man's Country on West 15th Street. Bette Midler was on stage with the heart throb Barry Manilow at the piano. Afterwards, I got plenty of personal attention in the rear of the Everlast truck from a sweet married lawyer named Lawrence, in town for a legal aid conference. What a passionate kisser. He wanted to take me back to Grinnell, Iowa, as if he could hide me from his family in the garden toolshed in his backyard. He'd sneak out and fuck me over the wheelbarrow. He was super-square, but really nice and very well hung.

TUESDAY APRIL 20, 1982

Daniel's painting class today at New York University is on the still life. We can pick any style we love. I'm torn between Chardin's romantic bowls of fruit and hanging game and Morandi's elegant abstract arrangements of bottles and ceramic mugs. They are so different, yet I love them both. I settled on the Chardin.

Tim was by my side in class. It was a comfort just to have him nearby. I asked him if he'd still be interested in the poetry session I promised him. He said absolutely. He thought I'd forgotten. So after class we walked downtown to my loft. Tim got hot and sweaty and took off his tank top. Of course, he got me aroused. I decided to ignore Terrence's advice from therapy. "Hey Tim, want some head? You know I feel cheated. You got away. You look to die for in those cutoffs." With that declaration, Tim opened his fly and shed the cutoffs; I pulled his jockstrap down and devoured his perfect cock whole.

After a long oral scene on the bed, I suggested we take a break and read some homoerotic lines from Allen Ginsberg's epic poem Howl. It included a favorite line of mine I wanted Tim to read aloud: "who let themselves be fucked in the ass by saintly motorcyclists, and screamed with joy." I knew Tim was strictly oral. I asked him to recite again Ginsberg's line about the pleasure of anal sex. "Visualize the scene. Put yourself in it. Pretend I'm the saintly motorcyclist standing next to you. I'm the guy who wants to fuck you. You are the beautiful boy with the gorgeous butt that everyone longs after, the butt of their dreams. Relax. Show me your hot butt. Let me touch you gently. Relax Tim, trust me. Recite Allen's line one more time. "who let themselves be fucked in the ass by saintly motorcyclists, and screamed with joy." Feel it. I won't hurt you. Show me your beautiful butt. I want to give you Allen's special gift for us queers. Can you accept Allen's gift? Relax Tim."

I stripped and put on a condom. I lubed up and took Tim on his first anal trip. I showed him the stars. I made him a man. He moaned. The pain slowly turned into the deepest pleasure. Tim asked for more. I made him a stud. Tim would never be the same. "Let's thank Allen for this one, from one poet to another. That's it Tim. Relax. Take it all in. You're a real stud now. That's beautiful. Let's thank Allen one more time." "who let themselves be fucked in the ass by saintly motorcyclists, and screamed with joy and screamed with joy."

WEDNESDAY APRIL 21, 1982

It's my older brother Mark's birthday. He's also an architect; he's two years older than me. He lives in an even larger loft in Soho with his girlfriend Chrisy. He's been especially nice to me since Jim and I broke up. Jim and my brother both went to Princeton, so they really connected. He invited me over for his pasta carbonara which is out of this world. He played The Moody Blues for me on his impressive sound system. He knows I love them. I gave him a three-volume set of small books containing Colin Rowe's lecture series from Cornell. Colin is a brilliant gay British architectural historian. Mark seemed good. We all had a wonderful time together. It made me realize once again how different our lives are.

THURSDAY APRIL 22, 1982

Therapy session number eleven.

"So, how are you Terrence? I'm sorry about our last session. I was depressed. Too lonely. But I had a breakthrough. I realized I never grieved properly for Jim and me. No one did. That wasn't right. Afterall, we had a loving relationship for almost nine years."

"Miles, you are right. I'm truly sorry."

Anyway, I'm much better. Our first session of "Sex & Poetry was a big hit. It was largely my baby. I'm proud of that. The guys really enjoyed themselves. Then on Sunday I went to the baths and had a good time with a sweet out-of-towner. I've been painting more. And yesterday I spent time with my brother and his girlfriend.

The big story was from Tuesday after painting class. I seduced Tim in my loft while reading him poetry. I introduced him to those homoerotic lines in Ginsberg's epic poem Howl. "...who let themselves be fucked in the ass by saintly motorcyclists, and screamed with joy." The poem is about the joy of anal sex, which I agree with completely. Tim came around in the end. I think I mentioned to you that before this Tim was strictly oral—100%. I think he was afraid of anal sex. Well, Tim had a major breakthrough. I butt-fucked him nice and slow. He was a virgin. It was his first time. He needed that. He was too uptight. Tim's twenty-one with a to-die-for butt. I turned him into a real stud overnight. I was super gentle. I fucked him real slow so he'd be ready when someone else treats him rough. I wanted him to experience firsthand the anal pleasure Ginsberg writes about in Howl. Tim needs to be comfortable with all forms of queer sex.

"Terrence, do you think I did the right thing with Tim?"

"Perhaps. It's hard to judge. You certainly treated Tim like an adult gay man. You taught him an important gay lesson. You showed him tenderness, love and concern."

"So tell me again Miles, why did your relationship with Jim fail?" The sex was lousy. The same was true with Robert.

"If our sex lives are in serious trouble, our relationships are doomed to failure as well. Hot sex makes for a happy relationship. Someday Tim will thank you,"

"Yes, you're right Terrence. It's always all about sex for all of us if we are completely honest with ourselves. I crave hot sex shared deeply with another man. A man whom I love. A man who loves me. God it is so difficult. How does anyone find their beloved?

"It's not easy, that's for sure. Don't give up Miles. Stay open to the possibility of love anywhere, at any time. Live in the present. I think you're doing just fine in a difficult situation."

Friday April 23, 1982

It was a beautiful sunny day. I had workday lunch with Bob outside; just takeout sandwiches on the plaza of the Seagram Building. I love the severity of the entry plaza with its grand sweep of several unbroken steps up to the plaza edge. The giant pavement slabs of pink granite, the pair of reflecting pools on each side and the massive blocks of green marble that form the benches we are sitting on to eat our sandwiches. It is like entering the forecourt to heaven.

Bob was concerned about me. He's worried I might do something foolish like jump off the subway platform in front of an incoming train to do myself in. I assured him I'm not that desperate yet, but things could always change. We had a few laughs.

Saturday April 24, 1982

On my way downstairs for coffee, I ran into Billy in our elevator. He looked amazing. He was in his signature outfit: black leather jacket with tattered blue jeans and old sneakers. But what was a complete surprise was his shaved head. "Billy, you look fantastic. I really love the new look. Super-hot." "Thanks Miles. I had it waxed yesterday at the shop in Astor Place. Are you busy? We should have a little fun and christen it. Plus, I owe you one from Sex & Poetry." "Well Billy, to tell you the truth, I have a secret fantasy where you have the leading role. It goes back to the day we met at the subway entrance on Ann Street. Remember the shower in my loft?" "I sure do. You were checking me out. I hid my boner under the towel." "Well Billy, I kept looking at the beads of water glistening on your beautiful butt. I really wanted to kneel down and lick your cheeks dry." "God, I only wish you had Miles." "Really? That's nice to know. You know Billy, it's not too late. Feel like a nice hot shower? Get that beautiful shiny head of yours all wet? Maybe I could at last make love to that spectacular butt of yours."

Sunday April 25, 1982

After that intense hookup with Billy yesterday, I needed space to decompress. It's Sunday. I feel like a church service. St. Paul's Chapel at Broadway and Ann Street will do nicely. It's just around the corner. It's Episcopal, but that doesn't matter. I don't need a Catholic church this morning. St. Paul's is pretty inside and the organ is soothing. Perfect. As I sat there recalling Billy's beautiful smile, I kept thinking how special he is. I really love him. He's the younger brother I never had.

Monday April 26, 1982

I asked Angie over for dinner after work. I made my brother's carbonara pasta dish. It's easy and everybody loves it. Angie arrived on time with an Edward Gory book titled The Glorious Nosebleed. We both enjoy his dry gay sense of humor. Jim and I used to always see him in his red Keds with his latest boyfriend during intermissions at the New York City Ballet in Lincoln Center. It feels like ages ago.

My life would be so simple if I were only straight. I'd ask Angie to marry me, hopefully she'd have me and we would live happily ever after. She's just the most spectacular woman I've ever met.

Angie told me she wants me to meet her favorite uncle Philip who works in New York's fashion industry. He lives in a renovated modernist apartment on Park Avenue which Angie designed. I assume Philip is gay. Unfortunately, he's quite a bit older than me. After being burned by older men like Jim, I'm thinking maybe I should be looking for someone my own age.

Tuesday April 27, 1982

In painting class today Daniel had us do some quick color study exercises in which we quickly painted the same simple subject four times using different color palettes. I chose a classic frontal view of a nude male torso shown four times in a vertical quadrant layout 24" x 36". Sort of a repetitive Andy Warhol feel; of course, it's one of my favorite subjects. No heads or arms on the torsos, just zoomed in views of tight pecs, gorgeous abdominals and massive muscular legs with the soft cocks dead center. Like the marble torsos I saw in the museums in Rome. Daniel was very impressed. He actually offered to buy it for $100, but I wanted to keep it for myself. My first queer painting.

WEDNESDAY APRIL 28, 1982

I had sex on the brain all day in the office. No surprise. Must be my queer cock painting. I decided to skip dinner and go directly from work to the New Saint Mark's Baths at St. Mark's Place in the East Village. I'm so horny I could literally screw a watermelon. Well, that wasn't necessary. While cruising the back hallway, I spotted this cute short chunky Puerto Rican kid named Jose lying nude on his stomach with his door ajar. What a butt on this kid! Small, plump, soft brown orbs. I couldn't help myself. Afterwards, we talked in bed for an hour, his smooth muscular body in my arms. He was a really sweet kid.

THURSDAY APRIL 29, 1982

My twelfth therapy session with Terrence. He jumped right in.

"Miles, I have to tell you before we get started, you look great! Your smile is really beautiful. You should smile more often." I turned beet red. He really made me blush. I opened up.

"Terrence, I confess, for the first time since Jim left me, I'm feeling more confident. My sexual encounters of late fall into two categories. First, there are the speechless, raw encounters often in dark backrooms or bath houses, fueled by pure lust and animal desires. No real connection is made, only an erotic memory to jerk off to later. And then there are equally hot encounters where eye contact and smiles and names are exchanged, where sexual desires are discussed, where affections are expressed and maybe I get to know something real about my partner, maybe plant the seed of a real relationship. I've wasted too much time with the former. I need to strive for the latter. I had a positive encounter with Billy last week. Sure we had sex, but more than that I realized I love Billy like a younger brother. I really care about him."

"Miles, what do you think this means in your quest to find Mr. Right, your next beloved?" I told him I'm more open to connecting with strangers. Just taking the time out to get to know them as fellow human beings, especially since as gay men we already share so many similar experiences coming out. We're potential best friends before we utter a word.

"Where should you look for Mr. Right?" I told him I was still grappling with that question. I told him about the Porto Rican kid Jose from the baths last night. He's not relationship material. Just gay candy. But I still love him. He's a beautiful young man. I respect him, even though I understand the limitations. Mr. Right could be anywhere really. I just have to keep looking, stay open to the possibility. Pay attention.

"Nice work Miles. You make me proud."

FRIDAY APRIL 30, 1982

I woke up early and decided to walk across the Brooklyn Bridge to Brooklyn Heights. Jim and I used to do it in reverse, with the backdrop of lower Manhattan in front of us, its image burned into my brain as a sharp memory. Our old street Remsen, a half block from the Promenade, looked unchanged from three years earlier; still lined with stoops up to the towering brownstones with their pretty flower boxes. I reflected back on our quiet domestic life there for three years in the all-white fourth floor walkup. It always felt more like Beacon Hill than Brooklyn. Manhattan was in another universe altogether.

Brooklyn Heights fit in well with our domestic bliss, safely tucked away from the steamy homosexual lusts of the West Village. No guys in black leather strutting the Promenade, a hand on a hot ass. I speculated what

84

life would be like now if Jim and I had never left Brooklyn. Would I have eventually answered the pulsing call of West Village cock anyway?

Afterall, I remind myself; it was Jim's sexy friend Gordon from Princeton who arranged the West Village outing that ended up in the backroom of the Stud, my hardon in a stranger's mouth. That was the introduction that would change my life forever. Wasn't that the spark that lit the blaze of erotic adventures that followed? No wonder I found the loft in Manhattan shortly thereafter. On my walk this morning, Brooklyn Heights looked unchanged, only now a bit staler, like a spinster aunt's old apartment with its plastic-covered sofas and the stench of time long passed. Manhattan was still my calling.

SATURDAY MAY 1, 1982

I had a serious workout at the Chelsea Gym. The works, I was there for three hours. Ran into Chuck. He mostly shows up for the action in the steam room. I'm trying to watch it, stay in control, but it's next to impossible. Chuck dragged me into the steam room. Plenty of action there. Of course, it's Saturday and it's raining outside. Chuck and I lounged around on the teak benches, talking, taking in the fresh hot steam. He told me his partner John doesn't mind if he fools around on the side. They have an open relationship like most gay couples. I always have a problem with that. If I truly love someone, my future husband, why would I let someone else explore their body. Chuck thinks I'm too possessive. He thinks I'm out-of-touch with today's hip gays. I don't really care. When I find my gorgeous Mr. Right, he's going to be all mine 24/7.

SUNDAY MAY 2, 1982

It's exactly three months since Jim left. It feels a lot longer. I'm anything other than religious, but this morning I felt like attending church services again. But this time it had to be a Catholic High Mass. It would have to be at St. Patrick's on Fifth Avenue. I wanted pomp and ceremony. I hadn't been in years. Jim always preferred Episcopal services since they were more gay-friendly, their services more theatrical. I was raised a good Catholic—

no fish on Fridays, Saturday confession, Sunday High Mass, but I was never a true believer. Now, I occasionally go to St. Patrick's, mostly for the architecture and the young priests in their black robes, their rosary beads dangling from the leather belts around their trim waists. They are often cute and very sexy like my Venetian priest. I missed him more than I realized. St. Patrick's could never yield the same erotic mystery. It's too big, too impersonal, a warehouse for the faithful. San Giovanni Grisostomo was tiny, so thrilling, so sensual. I remember the two of us were there all alone in a shaft of sunlight, transfixed lovers. We made passionate love surrounded by angels.

MONDAY MAY 3, 1982

After work Bob and I headed down to the Soho art revival cinema. They're showing the 1970 William Friedkin film The Boys in the Band based on the Off-Broadway play by Mart Crowley. I first saw it at Cornell with Bob when we were in our junior year. It's really terrific. Robert La Tourneaux plays Tex the cowboy birthday present for Harold. It always formed my picture of what it would be like living in Manhattan as an out gay man surrounded by my gay buddies. These guys weren't lonely. They sure knew how to have fun. In many respects it was quite accurate. Even Jim liked it, and he's impossible to please when it comes to queer cinema.

TUESDAY MAY 4, 1982

Daniel's painting class was another color palette exercise. I decided to do a companion piece to complement last week's frontal torso painting that Daniel went bonkers over. I chose the same quadrant format, but this time I painted the derriere, four guy's butts. I really got carried away. They were all beautiful—plump and fleshy. Well, you can imagine, Daniel went nuts. He raised his offer to $300 for the pair of paintings. I said sure, why not, I could always paint another set. It got me thinking, maybe I should do a second pair, front and back again, but this time present the guys clothed a bit. You know, something like a jock strap, bicycle spandex, Levi cutoffs, or just snug black leather chaps over old faded blue jeans. Sounds kind of hot. I'll have a ball.

Wednesday May 5, 1982

At lunch I ran over to MoMA to see the Bruce Weber show in the photography gallery. SOM are corporate sponsors, so employees get free admission. It was mostly his black and white male nudes, all-American hunks to drool over. I guess they are models. Bruce is only five years older than me. Seems like he has it all figured out already. He's way ahead of me. Bruce's men all look so relaxed, hanging out at the beach together. Naked. Clowning around like best buddies. Looks like a lot of casual gay sex. It's a glimpse into gay heaven. Sure made for a nice lunch break.

Thursday May 6, 1982

This was my 13th therapy session with Terrence.

"How's your week been going?" I've been trying to keep myself busy, staying out of trouble. You know, that for me, that isn't always easy. I've been painting a bit; I did a quadrant butt painting with sexy clothing that I'm intrigued with. Is it art or porn? For me it is definitely art, but my family of Catholics would call it porn.

I also spent an afternoon in my old neighborhood in Brooklyn Heights. It brought back fond memories of Franco, my afternoon fuck buddy I had on the side when Jim and I first moved there, before I had a job. Every Tuesday afternoon we'd meet up at his apartment near the Promenade. It was his day off from the Italian bank on Wall Street. Franco was always looking for a horny top. Lucky me. Such a nice guy and a gorgeous body. Broken English. Adorable.

"So, you and Jim had an open relationship?" Well, sort of. I saw Franco regularly for a few months, Jim saw his Princeton buddy Gordon a few times a year when he passed through New York. I wouldn't call either a relationship. More like a little fun between sex buddies.

"Is that how you envision your future once you find your Mr. Right?" Honestly not. I'd expect total fidelity on both our parts. Mr. Right will be altogether different—my soul mate, my sex idol, my everything.

"How's work? I heard through a friend that Simon was layoff." It was horrible. He started weeping uncontrollably. It was very upsetting. I really like Simon. Outside the office we've had some good times. You remember, Simon introduced me to the Mine Shaft. That was the night I met Jack.

"Oh yes, I recall the session vividly. Any plans for getting together with Simon?" Sure, I'm taking him out for dinner next Monday. He may want to fool around somewhere. Nothing too crazy. I'll look after him.

"Remember Miles, always play safe. Have a good week."

FRIDAY MAY 7, 1982

My older brother Mark broke up with his girlfriend Chrisy. I was sad because I really liked her. I invited her down to my loft for a simple pasta dinner. The deserted neighborhood at night really freaked her out. My building is the cast-iron Bennett Building, at Nassau and Fulton. It was used for filming the Brian De Palma psycho thriller Dressed to Kill starring Michael Caine. As a single-woman, all alone, Chrisy never felt safe.

SATURDAY MAY 8, 1982

I've been a good boy. No nothing. As a reward I figured I'd check into the New Saint Mark's Baths again. It's been ten days since my special encounter with sweet Jose. It was a cold rainy night. Inside, my sex encounter was just the opposite of the one with Jose. A butch leatherman cornered me in the steam room and wouldn't take no for an answer. He played rough without so much as a thank you. A little too rough. Just down and dirty. A creep. And then, to top things off, while I was walking back home from the East Village in the rain I was mugged by three street punks. They took my watch and money and my precious Briggs umbrella. I bought the Briggs in the Burlington Arcade on my first trip to London with Jim. So, it was extra special. Instantly furious and getting soaked in the rain, I sprinted up to the punk and grabbed the umbrella back. "You fucking asshole! That's my Briggs umbrella, you fuck head! Go to hell, you asshole!" They scattered like a pack of rats.

SUNDAY MAY 9, 1982

I spent most of the day working out in the Chelsea Gym. This nice guy Tony offered to spot me on the chest press and then we paired up to exercise together. He was great. Sexy Italian stud. Way more muscles than me, but very modest. A super nice guy, like the guys you see all over Rome. We worked out together for hours. He really pushed me. Of course, we checked each other out in the steam room afterwards. Very nice indeed. We traded blowjobs. We had burgers at the Empire Diner. I took his number for the box on my desk.

MONDAY MAY 10, 1982

My dinner out with Simon. My treat. He was a wreck. We went to Jane Street Seafood. Simon started crying. We hugged. I told him to update his resume and make sure to stress his experience at SOM. I mentioned I had a contact at Der Scutt that he should look into. They are supposedly very busy.

Then, out of the blue, Simon asked if I could arrange a threesome with Douglas. He knew Douglas lived in my building and was a good friend of mine. He'd seen him at the Mine Shaft and really has the hots for him. I told him I'd run the idea by Douglas. He's always looking for some fresh action. That cheered Simon up instantly.

TUESDAY MAY 11, 1982

Today's painting class was a challenge. Daniel asked us to paint our self-portrait. He provided mirrors. Staring at myself for so long was a little disconcerting. I started to feel like the guy in the mirror was not me, maybe somebody else. A little creepy. Anyway, it ended up rather odd. The face was a dark pink with yellow and green paint smears, rather German expressionist. I'm wearing a black leather vest over a bare chest. My hair is painted black, even though it's brown. The oddest thing is I gave myself a bushy black mustache, as if I was a butch leatherman. Terrence will be interested in this.

WEDNESDAY MAY 12, 1982

I started reading Dicken's Great Expectations; the Penguin edition. I read a chapter or two each day on my lunch hour at SOM. I sit on the plaza at either Lever House or the Seagram Building. Jim always encouraged me to read more, especially Dickens, Jane Austin, even Marcel Proust. Proust was the best.

THURSDAY MAY 13, 1982

My 14th therapy session with Terrence.

"What made you grab your umbrella out of the mugger's hand?" I went a little crazy. Not the smartest move in retrospect. He could have pulled out a knife. I was just furious that he grabbed for himself something of mine that I loved, that had deep associations. He would probably have ended up tossing it in a trash heap somewhere. He's not the kind of fellow who carries a Briggs umbrella.

"That sounds rather elitist on your part." You bet it does. Muggers are low lives, the lowest of the low. I was mugged once before in Brooklyn Heights by a conman. It was on Remsen Street in front of our apartment building. It was quiet; I was home mid-day for some reason. He said he needed $20 bus fare to get home. I handed him a crisp new $20 bill. Once I realized I had been had, he vanished suddenly in a split second.

90

"How did that make you feel?" Crummy actually. It told me you can't just be kind to strangers. You can get burned. I wanted to show kindness and respect to everyone. It was a bitter lesson. Even today I resent that.

"How do you mean?" I guess it is most obvious during my sexual encounters with strangers. I approach each as I'd hope they would approach me—with kindness, affection, respect, even love. Usually, they respond in kind. We share beautiful intimacy. Maybe we become friends, maybe we part knowing we'll never see each other again, but a precious memory has been formed. But sometimes, thankfully quite rarely, I meet someone who lies to me, manipulates me, to get me to do something I'd never do on my own. I'm used, raped, tossed aside, treated shabbily with no humanity. It makes me cry. I want to be open and loving to everyone, but that's naïve and foolish. I don't want to become some jaded old bitter queen. I've seen plenty of them hanging out in gay bars, garish and coarse. They frighten me. That's partly why I love young innocent boys. They are playful, alive, loving, trusting. I just want to take care of them, protect them from the monsters that are out there.

"Tell me about your self-portrait. Daniel mentioned it. He was terribly impressed." Well, I just let go completely and painted it from my heart. It doesn't really look a whole lot like me, but it feels more like who I aspire to become: I'm a boy, I'm a man, a street hustler, an angel, a devil, a bad ass. I'm still very much a work in progress. I need my next beloved to give my life a real center.

"Nice work today Miles."

Friday May 14, 1982

Bob told me that there are rumors around the office that the senior SOM partner Tyrell has been spotted inside the Ramrod, the leather bar on West Street near the Hudson. I'm going to check it out tonight. It was once a seamen's waterfront tavern before catering to butch gays in the 70s. I showed up around midnight in my leather motorcycle jacket. No sign of

Tyrell, but I spotted this skinny sexy guy posing at the pool table.

"Hi, my name is Jed." He gives me a warm friendly smile; then he offers to buy me a beer. He's dressed just like me. You'd think we were twins. It's almost funny. Jed doesn't mind in the least. I think he actually likes it; it seems to turn him on. He starts calling me "twin" affectionately. Jed is twenty-six, he jokingly calls me "old man." Then he tells me he's only attracted to older men. When I tell him I'm thirty-one, he tells me I'm in luck, that's the cutoff age. Obviously, Jed is really cute, totally relaxed, funny, just what I need right now. We start petting each other like kids, a squeeze here, a kiss there, a long feel down low, a genuine hug. My head is spinning. Jed asks me if I'd like a ride on his Harley out front. "Absolutely. Where to?" "How about my loft on Canal Street; let's have some fun." I'm all in. How could anyone refuse Jed? He's just the sweetest guy on earth. A breeze of fresh air. It was a tremendous night. Jed was so easy going. So easy to please. A sweet gentle guy. He was absolutely beautiful.

SATURDAY MAY 15, 1982

I need to see some great art. I decided to do the Soho galleries solo. Jim and I did them often together on weekends. There is a dedicated crowd of gallery goers in Soho, straight and gay. They follow the galleries religiously. That was Jim and me. Leo Castelli, Mary Boone, Gagosian, Max Protetch to name a few. Plus, large scale permanent installations like Walter De Maria's The Broken Kilometer on West Broadway. 500 solid brass rods, each two meters long by two inches thick, arranged perfectly in five rows of 100 rods each. It's gorgeous. Plus, today as a special treat, I got to see recent giant screen print portraits by Andy Warhol at Leo Castelli: Marilyn, Jackie, Mick Jagger, Twiggy, Chairman Mao. They were all beautiful.

SUNDAY MAY 16, 1982

I was feeling lonely. Jed wasn't around. I went alone to a matinee performance of Ridley Scott's Blade Runner, which was just released. It was shown on a giant screen at the Ziegfeld. It was great; I loved the futuristic sets. Deckard (Harrison Ford) and Rachel (Sean Young) made the perfect romantic couple. I would have gladly played the part of Rachel opposite Harrison. Ford is so dreamy, sensitive and strong. What a movie! And the music by Vangelis was awesome.

Afterwards on my way home, outside the Bennett Building, I ran into Billy. I hadn't seen him in three weeks, since his shower in my loft. He looked great. He asked me if I had any dinner plans. He wanted to take me out to Chinatown. His treat; sort of a long overdue thank you. I was touched. Over Szechuan he filled me in. Since April 1st he has a new job in the Mayor's office, as chief assistant in charge of the delivery of city services for the homeless. Wow! I was impressed. "Billy, that's fabulous! I'm so proud of you. Congratulations!" "It's a lot more satisfying than working on Wall Street. It was a trial job offer. They wanted to make sure I could handle the responsibility. I told them I'm up for the challenge. Anyway, it all worked out. I'm so relieved. I feel like I'm getting my life back. And it's all thanks to you." "Nonsense Billy. I'm so happy I met you."

Over dessert I asked Billy how his personal life was going. He's terribly lonely. More than a bit like me. In his previous life, he used to live in the gay sex clubs every night, fucking his brains out with strangers. He knows that's not the answer. But how can he meet regular friendly guys? Then, out of nowhere, he mentioned the Gay Men's Health Crisis (GMHC). He's thinking of enrolling in their Buddy Program to assist PWAs (People with AIDS). It's only been going a few months. Would I like to join him? I started crying. "Thank you for asking me Billy. Yes I would. I should have gotten involved sooner. You're a better man than me. Thank you Billy." "Great Miles. Let's go to their Monday night meeting tomorrow night and sign up. Their office is on West 22nd Street." "Wow. Billy now it's your turn to save me." We hugged in the middle of the restaurant. We both cried tears of thanks.

MONDAY MAY 17, 1982

I let Simon know our threesome with Douglas tonight was off. I told him Billy and I had already signed up for the GMHC Buddy Program. We have our intake interview on Wednesday. Simon was stunned. I encouraged him to join us. Simon said he wasn't ready yet. He can't face AIDS. It's too close to home.

When I told Douglas he confessed he's already a member of GMHC. He planned to tell me soon. He loves it. The guys are all great. He feels better getting involved. He helps out on the AIDS Hotline. He welcomed Billy and me aboard. How exciting! For the first time in months, I felt like my life may have a purpose. I can't wait to tell Terrence.

TUESDAY MAY 18, 1982

In Daniel's painting class tonight, he asked us to only use black and white, no color. Explore figure ground relationships. I immediately thought of the black and white Mapplethorpe photo Marty and Hank which I had just seen the night before hanging on a wall at GMHC. It showed a sexy blowjob with the black guy's cock inside the white guy's mouth. The white guy's eyes are closed. He's in heaven. It was perfect. In my version I added white highlights on the black guy's gorgeous oiled body and gave the white guy a black leather vest. Daniel was really impressed.

It somehow made us think of AIDS, of the world we live in today, of men loving men in crisis. We all have a deep connection to each other through our queer sex. It doesn't matter if we're healthy or sick, young or old, black or white. Mapplethorpe captures that connection.

Daniel announced that next week May 25th will be our last class painting together. We can paint anything we like, but it should be something we really love.

WEDNESDAY MAY 19, 1982

Billy and my first visit to GMHC. We were there for our Buddy Program interviews with a cool black guy named Damian. The office was busy with a dozen guys seated on the floor in a circle. It was noisy. Damian took us to an empty office so we could talk. First thing Damian did was give each of us a warm bear hug. "Thank you for coming. Welcome to GMHC." He told us all about the Buddy Program. "There are no fixed rules. Just remember to always show your Buddy love and he will be your greatest fan. I've seen it work every time. It's beautiful."

Damian assigned Patrick to me. I can't wait to meet him. He's twenty-three, a former dancer in the Corp de ballet of the New York City Ballet. He lives alone in a West Village walk-up on Perry Street. He's on leave from the dance company. Lonely and depressed. Needs help with daily chores. Craves friendship. Has a cat named Mandy. Billy's buddy is named Sean. He just turned thirty-four. He's a retired AIDS lawyer on full disability. He has early Kaposi Sarcoma, purple skin lesions, or KS. He doesn't want to be seen outside on the sidewalk. He's a hermit. Lives on Bank Street in one of those white glazed brick high-rises in the West Village. He's a proud Texan.

THURSDAY MAY 20, 1982

Tonight's therapy session with Terrence is my 15th. I can't wait to tell him about the GMHC Buddy Program.

"Wow! That's big news. Why did you join now?" I'm overdue, don't you think? About time I did something selfless for a change. Time to grow up.

"Congratulations! I'm confident you will like it. I'm proud of you Miles. Let's have a hug."

"I also have news. I think you may be ready soon to advance to group therapy. In two or three weeks I will have an opening. It's a small group I limit to six guys maximum. Would you be interested? Think it over. Of course, everyone is gay; these guys are all in their 30s, four are single like you and two are in relationships. I think you'd be a good fit. What are your initial feelings?" I'm a little nervous. I really love the close relationship I have here with just you each week. I'm not sure I'll be able to open up so easily in a group.

"That's normal Miles. I think you'll make the adjustment easily. I hope you'll find your therapy mates supportive and loving. Bonding comes naturally. Group therapy is a wonderful way to discuss issues we are all going through." Terrence made me much more relaxed. It actually sounded great. I could imagine making new friends and discussing my issue of out-of-control anonymous sex. Terrence explained the only rules in his group therapy are no sexual relationships between mates as long as they are in the group, and total honesty. Simple right?

"Great! Let's move along. How has your week gone?" Actually, pretty good overall. I had dinner with Billy, the homeless guy I helped out. He's doing great. He has a job in the Mayor's office helping oversee the delivery of services for the homeless. He's lonely, a lot like me. It was his idea to join the GMHC Buddy Program.

"Otherwise, the only time I went out cruising, I met up with a real person named Jed at the Ramrod. We got to know each other a little before having sex. Jed's a really nice guy, gentle and warm, a lot of fun. He took me on my first motorcycle ride. It was tremendous! We were both in our motorcycle jackets, me in the back, my arms around Jed's torso to feel safe. I loved that part the most, more than the sex actually. It was just great, my nose in his thick black hair. I can trust Jed completely. I hope to see him again. I know he's not really looking for a long-term relationship right now, but I'd just like to hang out with him for a while. He's good for me and he's so cool.

"Tell me more about Jed. What attracted you to him initially?" Definitely his butch sexy look, work boots, ripped frayed Levi's, the old worn motorcycle jacket. The funny thing was we were both dressed exactly the same. Jed called me "twin." We are similar ages, 31 and 26. It got me thinking, should my Mr. Right be my age, look similar, dress in the same style? Maybe so.

"You said the sex was all right. Not super-hot?" That's true. But it didn't matter at all. He made my head spin. I would have been content just to hold him in my arms all night long. The actual sex was unimportant."

"Sounds like an important experience for you. Would you agree?" Yes Terrence, absolutely. I felt proud of myself, like I had treated a future beloved the right way, with total respect. I know Jed is not the one, but he comes the closest so far.

"Very good work Miles."

FRIDAY MAY 21, 1982

I called up Patrick to set up a time and place to meet. It made no difference to me, but I wanted to give him a few choices. Any restaurant or bar would be fine. I could come to his apartment or he could come down to my loft. Whatever he preferred. To my surprise he suggested the leather bar the Ramrod. I told him that was fine with me. I go there often myself. I like the friendly butch crowd. I guess he does as well. When I asked him to describe himself, he said that was easy. "I'll be the only guy with red hair wearing lots of leather." When he asked me to describe myself, I said I'd dress up for the occasion in my black and red motorcycle jacket and ratty old Levi's. He chuckled and said he couldn't wait to meet me. He asked if I liked cats. "Are you kidding? Is the pope Catholic?"

We hit it off immediately. I guess I passed the butch test in the Ramrod. Patrick is super cute and super butch as well. The Irish edition of Jed. It will be a real challenge for me to keep my hands out of Patrick's skin-tight pants.

We sat in a back booth and talked for over an hour—our back stories, college days, relationships, our favorite Balanchine ballets. Patrick grew up in rural Iowa and went to Grinnell College. He ran away to New York City at eighteen. Lincoln Kirstein picked him up in the Eagle, fondled him for a week, and then put him in the Corp de ballet of the New York City Ballet. That lasted three years before he contracted AIDS fooling around with the other dancers, ending up on full disability two years ago. He hopes the GMHC Buddy Program is a lifeline. He's exhausted half the time. The only good news is Patrick still has over 600 T-cells.

"I think I'm gonna get you out of here. How about a taxi to the Empire Diner for a bowl of their Grandma's chicken soup, then home to bed? If you're a good boy, I'll tell you a dirty bedtime story. Sound good?" "Honestly, it sounds like I fell into shit. Gee, thanks for everything Miles."

SATURDAY MAY 22, 1982

I spent most of Saturday morning at the Chelsea pumping iron. There was a good crowd. No sign of Tony, my Italian gym buddy from a few weeks ago. I missed him. We had a great time together. I'm finally starting to get a gym bod. Even my six-pack abs are starting to show.

In the steam room I kept thinking of Patrick. Great kid. I want to help him. Hands off. He's mighty cute, but no touching the merchandise. I noticed last night that his refrigerator was empty. After a little anonymous steam room sex, I dressed and went grocery shopping at Balducci's. I intend to spoil the kid.

SUNDAY MAY 23, 1982

I put in a few hours of overtime Sunday morning at SOM. Bob was there as usual. We had corned beef sandwiches together at Carnegie Deli. I told him all about the GMHC Buddy Program and Patrick. I have established a routine where I will visit Patrick three times a week helping him with groceries, laundry and long visits. He really enjoys the attention, just like Damian predicted.

Bob was terribly impressed. He told me he's convinced I'm ripe to find my Mr. Right. Just hang in there. From Bob's mouth to God's ears.

Monday May 24, 1982

I had my annual SOM performance review today. They called me into the main conference room with the sliding frosted glass doors closed. Three senior staff were already seated opposite me all alone. It felt like I was before a firing squad. For me they matched up the Senior Partner Tyrell, my immediate supervisor Paul and Roy who heads up the interiors department. Was that really just a coincidence? They are all gay. What luck I just happened to be wearing my tightest old pair of faded chinos that show off my dick nicely. It must have done the trick. Everyone was very friendly, very complimentary. They gave me a 6% raise. I'm such a slut.

Tuesday May 25, 1982

Tonight, will be my last painting class with Daniel. He brought a chocolate layer cake from Rocco's to acknowledge the momentous occasion. We all stood up to sing "For He's a Jolly Good Fellow" embellished with whoops and hollers. I did another cock painting, this time fully erect. I opted for a medium size cock. It looked almost real. Passionate pinks, reds and oranges for the shaft and head. Framed all around by frayed tattered denim, pale blues faded to snow white at the edges. Silvery Levi fly buttons for a little contrast. Plus, a studded leather cock ring for erotic detail. I couldn't deny it was pornographic. Call a spade a spade. It was a horizontal painting, 24" x 36". I could tell Daniel really wanted it, so when things winded down, I handed it to him as my gift and thanked him for being such a great painting instructor.

Wednesday May 26, 1982

Jim called me up in the office. He asked me out for dinner tonight at his favorite Mexican restaurant in the West Village around the corner from the Stud. Sure, why not? We hadn't seen each other in ten weeks. Jim looks great. He and Sandy tentatively plan to leave the end of July on their cross-country U-Haul drive to San Francisco. They have an apartment lined up in the Mission District. Jim quits his New York City job at Putnam Publishing on June 30th. He and Sandy are renting a house in Cherry Grove the second and third weeks of July. He invited me out anytime during that period. Jim clearly wants to remain friends. We hugged outside the restaurant and said good night. I took a pass on the Stud.

Thursday May 27, 1982

Therapy session #16 with Terrence.

"How are you feeling Miles?" I'm frustrated and excited at the same time. I keep looking for Mr. Right. I know he's out there. I just have to be patient and he'll turn up. Bob at work suggested a personal ad in The Native. That's not my style. It's nonvisual. I'm super visual. I have to see the guy in the flesh, warts and all. His face, eyes, hair and hands are important. His clothing speaks volumes. Of course, his crotch and butt are of special interest. Is his body language relaxed and confident? Is he open? Does he smile a lot? Is he intelligent? Does he listen? Does he make me laugh? No wonder I haven't found Mr. Right. Maybe I need to cut the poor guy a little slack, you think?

"You said it first Miles. I'd have to agree. Nobody is perfect. But can you still love his imperfections?" I'll try my best. I realize I'm a control queen. I need to work on that.

"How so?" Jim used to tell me I was suffocating him with all my high expectations, my demands for perfection. Sometimes he just wanted to relax, play, make a mess. I get it from my mom Terry. With her, everything had to be totally perfect. Never a mess. Of course, I delivered the ultimate mess by turning out gay.

"But didn't you tell me Terry accepted you and Jim as a committed couple? Doesn't that tell you something." Yes, yes, you are right Terrence. Terry has changed over the years; she has come around. I need to give her more credit.

"You told me last week Jed was not interested in a long-term relationship at this time, correct? Was there anything else that ruled Jed out as a Mr. Right?" Yes, there is actually. His age. Jed is five years younger than me. Not a whole lot, but as a Mr. Right, it concerns me. Will he be able to show maturity when we face a difficult problem like being open with our families, discussing candidly all our sex outside the relationship, coming out at work? I'd rather he was five years older, than five years younger. Do you know what I mean?

"Yes, I certainly do. You make a good point Miles. Let's pick this up from here next week. Good work."

FRIDAY MAY 28, 1982

Jed called me at SOM. He wanted to have dinner with me tonight in the Village. He needed to talk. We met up at Jane Street Seafood. He told me he's been feeling awful, leading me on. He really likes me and doesn't want to hurt me. He has an older live-in boyfriend, Max; they've been together for five years. Max is crazy about Jed. He totally adores him. He accepts Jed's insatiable craving for outside sex in leather bars. Max is 52, twice the age of Jed's 26. Max is a quiet home body; he knows Jed will eventually come back home to him. He accepts their arrangement. I was surprised, but deeply touched at Jed's honesty. He showed real maturity. I insisted we remain close friends. I told him next time I want to meet his Max as well. Jed agreed. We hugged.

101

SATURDAY MAY 29, 1982

It's the start of the Memorial Day weekend. I don't have any big plans. Feeling rather lonely. It's raining. I decided to see Fassbinder's new homoerotic film Querelle, based on the Genet novel. It was playing at the Quad on 13th. It's a very small theater. I sat down in the middle next to a young guy who looked solo and as queer as a three-dollar bill. Navy green bomber jacket with the orange inner lining. This guy wore the jacket open over his bare chiseled chest. His button fly Levi's were ripped and faded, with no belt and the fly buttons conveniently left open. Not exactly subtle. We both pulled out our equipment and proceeded to jerk each other off using a little sex wax that he provided. He was huge. It was super-hot. We both came oceans urged on by the simmering sex scene on the big screen overhead. Afterwards, we just sat there and watched the rest of the film as if nothing unusual had happened. Outside on 13th Street it was still raining lightly. We parted with just a glance and a little smile in opposite directions without exchanging a word. The whole episode left me a little shaken. It felt dangerous and thrilling at the same time.

SUNDAY MAY 30, 1982

Bob and I met up in Julius' for a night of serious bar hopping in the West Village. We figured things should be busy Memorial Day weekend. We hit the Stud, the Eagle, the Ramrod, ending up at the Anvil. Bob knows them all; he's a leather queen. After a while, the guys all start to look the same, hyper-butch studs, not terribly friendly, not much going on upstairs and clearly overly impressed with themselves. Anyway, it was a giant washout. Zip! Maybe my requirements for a Marlboro Man as my Mr. Right are totally off the mark. Maybe that's my problem. Now I'm really confused.

MONDAY MAY 31, 1982

It was Memorial Day. At 6 o'clock I had an invitation to Chuck and John's for a traditional backyard barbeque at their townhouse on Gansevoort Street. It was already jumping when I showed up. There must have been at least thirty people, all ages. Chuck made sure the food was fabulous. He's a super cook. I stayed until nine.

Back at the loft I took a nap before heading out around midnight to the leather bars again—looking for Mr. Right. I did my usual circuit. Lots of guys out tonight. The backroom at the Stud was packed wall-to-wall. The cigarette smoke was a turn off. The Eagle had a Black Party with live kinky sex acts—not for me. Looking for something a little quieter and more humane, I dropped in to the Ramrod, half hoping to run into Jed, but of course, he had somewhere better to be.

Feeling depressed at having struck out yet again, I decided to walk back to the loft. It was getting chilly in my motorcycle jacket. At 23rd Street off of 8th I spotted the leather bar Maneuvers. Since it was starting to sprinkle, I figured I'd jump inside for a quick beer until the rain passed.

As I stepped inside the dimly lit interior, I noticed a couple standing at the bar talking, their backs to me. A couple of leathermen in biker gear were hanging out around a pool table in the back; the place was practically empty. One of the two guys at the bar turned so I could see him clearly. I was immediately mesmerized. He wasn't your usual leatherman. He really wasn't a leatherman at all. Sure, he wore the black leather jacket, the faded 501s, the red and black check lumberjack shirt, he had thick black hair, a black bushy moustache. But he was more relaxed in sneakers than in work boots. And most striking of all, his eyeglass frames were not just large, they were bright red, like an Andy Warhol model. He noticed me staring at him. He returned the stare with a faint smile.

I walked towards him, towards the bar, planning to order a beer. As I got near, the stranger's partner turned away headed to the back; I assumed to use the men's room. My stranger then turned abruptly to face me squarely. He then delivered to me, to me alone, the warmest open smile I'd ever seen. His shiny brown eyes were soft with kindness and life. Before I could even speak, the stranger rescued me. "Hi, I'm Abbey. Can I buy you a drink? Are you alright?" His deep voice left my head pleasantly numb, full of cotton, like when I had placed my small ear against a giant conch seashell as a boy.

In twelve simple words he had somehow touched my core. I was barely able to speak. My throat was dry; I was a basket case. At last, I spoke, on the verge of tears. "Please yes, thank you Abbey. I'm Miles. Please forgive me. I'm crying." "Nonsense, I'm flattered. You're real."

Abbey understood the situation immediately. He knew seconds were critical. He asked the bartender for a business card and pen. On the back he quickly wrote his name, address and phone numbers. He placed the card in my open hand and gently held it for just a moment as he spoke softly, "Please call me tomorrow evening Miles." "Yes, I will Abbey." As the second man returned from the rear, Abbey turned to leave with him. As he passed my side, just inches from my face, we exchanged eye contact for as long as possible. I whispered "Good night Abbey." As the front door opened, a blast of cold night air swept across my face.

TUESDAY JUNE 1, 1982

All day long I could think of nothing other than my brief encounter with Abbey. Who was this guy? He was unlike anyone I'd ever met. So relaxed and real. Sure, he was your classic West Village butch stud, but not so fast, he was his own man in those outrageous red framed glasses. A touch of Elton John at a leather party. He certainly captured my attention. First, I planned to call him at eight sharp tonight. Then I thought it would be better at seven. I finally settled on 7:30.

He picked up right away. His deep voice immediately made my head spin like the night before. It was extremely pleasant. I just wanted to listen to him talk, he could say almost anything, I just wanted that numbing sensation to go on forever. He asked me how I was doing. I told him I felt like I was flying, like Michael in Peter Pan. Abbey told me Peter Pan was his favorite musical as a little boy. His mother Shirley took him to see Mary Martin on Broadway when he was five. It was a highpoint of his childhood.

We talked for several hours. Abbey asked me to call him again on Wednesday night.

104

WEDNESDAY JUNE 2, 1982

Our second night on the phone we took turns talking about family stuff and significant relationships we'd had since coming out. We are practically the same age. What a relief after Jim. Abbey is just two months older than me.

Abbey told me all about his mom Shirley. She is divorced from Abbey's dad Eddie whom Abbey rarely sees. Eddie sold electronic equipment. Shirley is the temple administrator of a Jewish synagogue on the Upper East Side. She and Abbey are extremely close. She is very relaxed around gays; in fact, she marches with Abbey in the New York City Gay Pride Parade. The New York Times interviewed her on a feature story about gays and their parents. Abbey has older sisters, Susie and Janet. Apparently, Susie, a writer who lives in Boston, was instrumental in Abbey's coming out to his parents. She is bisexual. Abbey adores her. His older married straight sister Janet is an academic. She teaches anthropology at Florida International University. She spent three decades in the Amazon living with "her tribe." That's when she wrote her PhD.

Abbey's first long-term relationship was with Donald. It lasted three years. Donald introduced Abbey to opera, kicking and screaming, but he eventually came around to really love it. Abbey and Donald are still good friends. Julian came next for a similar length of time; in contrast, he was trouble from day one. Julian was from Jackson Beach, Florida; apparently a real firecracker. Their crazy landlady actually had him arrested at one point. Last was Joel, with his Irish Setter, a relationship which lasted almost one year. Joel was the guy standing next to Abbey in Maneuvers. That night, Abbey and Joel had just returned from a Memorial Day weekend in Provincetown. Apparently, it was a disaster. Joel baited Abbey into a bicycle race on the sand covered concrete paths through the dunes. It ended in a dreadful crash for Abbey who was covered in blood. Abbey told me he was amazed I hadn't noticed the dozens of scabs all over his body. I must have been fixated on his smile. He said he knew his relationship with Joel was over even before he saw me. The next day Abbey moved back into Shirley's apartment. That's where he's been while talking on the phone with me for hours.

Thursday June 3, 1982

I have my therapy session #17 with Terrence tonight which means I won't be able to talk to Abbey on the phone. But Abbey suggested he come down to my loft Friday after work following his regular Friday Shabbat dinner with his mom Shirley around 7 o'clock. That's much better than the phone. We can finally meet in person. Our first date.

"Miles, tell me all about Abbey. How are you feeling?" I'm flying like a kite. I realize I hardly know the guy, but I already feel so close to him. I told you his deep voice makes my head spin, even on the phone. I can't wait to hold him in my arms. It feels like love at first sight. Is that possible? I haven't felt like this since I met Jim in a gay bar in Ithaca almost ten years ago. But Abbey is so different from Jim. He's so sexy, so physical. He's so real, so relaxed. I need to slow down. We hardly know each other. I've only seen him for five minutes, though we did talk on the phone for over five hours.

"How does Abbey measure up to your picture of Mr. Right?" That's what is so remarkable. Abbey does not look exactly like the Marlboro Man, but somehow, he's even better, he's not just a clone copy, he's unique and real. Yes, he's still my dream butch leatherman with the thick black mustache, but he's much more, he's Abbey, he's his own man. I love those playful parts of him the most. His red glasses, his sneakers and his red and black lumberjack shirt are his alone. He's still a kid. I love that.

When I spoke to Abbey in Maneuvers, our eyes never parted. He stared into my eyes without blinking. I felt completely exposed, naked. I felt safe, like I could trust this stranger to take care of me, maybe to even love me.

Abbey listens. And he showed courage. He wasn't afraid to expose himself. He told me he smoked, even after I told him how much I hated the fact that my mother was a chain smoker. He promised me he'd never smoke in front of me. I told him I would support him in any way I could to help him to stop smoking. When I told him about Cornell, he confessed he was a college drop-out. It wasn't entirely his fault. Eddie's tuition check bounced.

I realized that this sweet guy had been dealt some very bad hands.

"How did those revelations make you feel?" First lucky, that my parents supported me 100% through college. Abbey didn't get that. I felt sorry for him. I wanted to help turn that around somehow. I wanted to right a wrong.

"Did you blame Abbey?" Not at all, he wasn't to blame. His parents let him down.

"Good work Miles. Be on your guard. Keep your communications with Abbey open and clear at all times. I know you can do it. I'm proud of you."

FRIDAY JUNE 4, 1982

How can I describe my first kiss with Abbey? First of all, it seemed to go on forever. It was part of an embrace that joined our bodies into one. We were standing in the middle of my loft as soon as he walked through the door. It started as an intimate smile. A shy introduction. A hesitant request. A sense of wonder, with my fingers on his thick moustache, in his soft curly hair. My tongue in his small warm ears. An extraordinary softness. I touched his fleshy lips with mine for the first time with the gentlest pressure. Parting them gave way to an intoxicating thrill. Wet pleasures and textures. My head blown wide open. Lost in heaven.

SATURDAY JUNE 5, 1982

After I cooked a breakfast of scrambled eggs and blue cheese, I took Abbey on his first guided tour of the Financial District: City Hall, the Woolworth Building, the World Trade Center, Chase Manhattan, Grace Cathedral and the New York Stock Exchange. Abbey told me all about the time he toured the Chase Manhattan Headquarters at Liberty Street when he was fourteen, four years after it opened in 1961. I told him it was designed by Gordon Bunshaft of SOM where I work. Abbey even got inside the main

Board Room on the 60th floor. He loved that building as much as I did. We kissed in an embrace under the four monumental black and white Jean Dubuffet trees. It was nice to discover that Abbey and I shared a love for modern architecture.

The rest of the day we spent in bed napping, sharing each other's most private secrets. I was already in love with Abbey.

SUNDAY JUNE 6, 1982

It was New York University graduation Day. I wanted to drop by and congratulate Tim. He plans to move to San Francisco in a week to start his new job at City Lights Booksellers. He will meet his hero, the poet Lawrence Ferlinghetti, and hopefully get some tips on his poetry. I wished him all the best and introduced him to Abbey. In parting I gave Tim a warm hug. "Congratulations Tim you sexy stud. I'll miss you. Please always play safe. Take good care of yourself buddy."

Abbey was a little down walking around New York University. I sensed it was connected to his story about dropping out of college. We stopped in Washington Square Park to sit down and talk. Abbey told me he felt overwhelmed. I told him we could fix all that, one day at a time. I'd support him 100%. If he was committed, I'd help him find a way. I told him to relax and to not think about it for now. No hurry.

We had a romantic dinner at Il Sabor. Near the end Abbey brought up the topic of our dating. He proposed initially sleeping over in my loft only on the weekends, Friday, Saturday and Sunday nights. The other workday nights he'd sleep at Shirley's and we could always talk on the phone. It made perfect sense, but, of course, I wanted more. I'm always so needy. Abbey was gentle, but firm. He wanted to take things a little slow, one step at a time. He told me he learned from several years in therapy that successful relationships are built on a foundation of clear communication that requires time. He wants our relationship to be strong and lasting. I told Abbey I would do as he asked. I trusted he knew what's best. I told

Abbey I will want to discuss this with Terrence on Thursday. Abbey had no problem with that at all. In fact, he encouraged it.

MONDAY JUNE 7, 1982

Back at SOM bright and early, I told Bob all about Abbey. He wants to meet him as soon as possible. He checked in with Dave. We're set for dinner on this Wednesday at Bob and Dave's apartment on Central Park West.

On tonight's phone call with Abbey, I told him all about Bob, how he's my best friend, my closest buddy, going back to my days at Cornell. Abbey told me he wants to meet all my friends, including Bob. Plus, he wants me to meet his mother Shirley and his best childhood buddy Jimmy. He felt strongly that relationships need supportive friends to succeed.

TUESDAY JUNE 8, 1982

It's our one-week anniversary. Abbey sent me a sweet card in the mail. I was really touched. It was a sunburst. It said how much he cared for me. He hasn't told me that he loves me yet, but that's okay. It's his style. Abbey is wise, he's very thoughtful. He's patient, unlike me. He's good for me. He makes me slow down a little. We don't have to have sex every day. A couple of times a week is fine. That way I'll be super horny. He's really something. I'm happy. I'm really falling for him. His deep voice still makes my head buzz.

WEDNESDAY JUNE 9, 1982

Abbey and I met up after work at the Orwell House on Central Park West and 86th Street. Bob and Dave live in a two-bedroom apartment on the second floor facing the park. It's a doorman building. What a contrast with the Bennett Building downtown. Orwell House is just six short blocks above the notorious Ramble, the park's main gay cruising grounds. I'd only been there in the daytime. It's best known for the night time edition. Bob is a regular.

Bob and Abbey hit it off instantly. I was so relieved. Bob is my closest New York City friend, and I really wanted Bob and Abbey to bond. When I was with Jim all those years, Dave and Jim didn't get along at all. Some nonsense about them both growing up in Grinnell, Iowa. It was ridiculous. As a result, I hardly saw Bob at the apartment. This new arrangement should be much better.

Afterwards, Bob took us for a walk down Central Park West to the Ramble, just for a peek. Guys were headed in. Bob said good night as he went inside to check things out, while Abbey and I walked down CPW, hand in hand, to Lincoln Towers where Shirley lives. I hugged Abbey on the sidewalk. As I mussed his soft hair. Abbey gave my butt a squeeze. I gave him a neck massage on a park bench. Kissing, we said good night.

Walking down Broadway to the loft I kept thinking about Bob and Abbey, my best old friend and my best new friend.

THURSDAY JUNE 10, 1982

Tonight, is my first group therapy session with Terrence. There are five guys in the group plus me. Terrence asked each of them to introduce themselves for my benefit. It was quite a mix. Steve is single, 30, a PhD economics grad student at New York University, super cute in his black leather jacket. He's definitely a leather queen. Graham, 32, is single, recently out and new to New York City. He works as an accountant on Lower Broadway. Brandon, 33, is a children's book editor, in an 8-year relationship with an older man named Jason, 42. Darko is 38, single, very shy and rather mysterious. Lastly Eric, 30, is a graphic designer in a 4-year relationship with Aaron, 32, who is also a graphic designer in the same firm. I then announced that I was Miles, 31, an architect with SOM, in a 10-day relationship with Abbey, the man of my dreams. With that I was given a standing ovation with cheers. I was touched.

Terrence asked me to please share my story of how I met Abbey. At first, I felt very awkward, but as I spoke to these guys, I could see in each of

110

their faces that they were clearly on my side, rooting for me; that each of them understood exactly where I was coming from. I felt their love. I opened up. I told them all about Jim, about our best years together, our sudden breakup, my four months of living alone looking for Mr. Right, the ups and downs, the painful lessons I learned along the way. By the time I stopped talking I was crying. I realized I had just found my new family.

Friday June 11, 1982

Abbey and I met up after work at the bookstore Three Lives and Company. I didn't want to meet him in a smokey bar like Julius' which is across the street. Jim and I used to always meet at Julius'; it was Jim's favorite bar. That's where he met Sandy when I was in Venice. I told Abbey the whole story.

Abbey was taking me to his favorite French restaurant Café de la Gare on Perry Street run by a lesbian named Marie and her assistant Jerry. Abbey knew them well. That was something I quickly noticed about Abbey. He connected with people. He always knew the names of the owners and waiters in his favorite restaurants, or the shopkeepers he'd frequent. He'd always take out time to chat with them. What a contrast with Jim, who rarely spoke to anyone who waited on him. I really admired that in Abbey. I timidly copied him. It felt right.

After dinner we walked thru Soho and Tribeca, down quiet Broadway to City Hall, to the Bennett Building. On our way in the back door we ran into Douglas who was leaving for the leather bars. I introduced Abbey. Douglas could tell right away we were a new couple in love. "Miles, congratulations, you look so alive. I wish both of you all the best." That was really nice. I asked Douglas if he'd come down for dinner sometime with Abbey and me. Just dinner, no sex. He chuckled. "Sure, I'd love to honestly." Later on, I told Abbey all about Douglas, how he helped me get through the worst of times when Jim walked out. Douglas has always been a good friend.

SATURDAY JUNE 12, 1982

Abbey keeps asking me about SOM, so I decided to just take him there on the weekend when it's quiet. Bob was there doing his usual overtime. After the grand tour, Abbey asked Bob how his trip to the Ramble went after we parted Wednesday night. Bob said he met this Swedish couple in New York City on vacation. After sex in the bushes, they got to talking and Bob invited them back to Orwell House. They talked for hours. That's Bob, he always bonds with strangers during sex and ends up with new friends whom he nurtures for years.

After SOM, I took Abbey to MoMA, as my guest on my SOM membership. He really loved the giant Jackson Pollocks and Philip Johnson's sculpture garden. Afterwards we did the Design Shop. Abbey is really into modern design. He enjoyed looking at the wristwatches.

Afterwards Abbey wanted to stop by Shirley's apartment in Lincoln Towers. She was out on Long Island for the day. She needed Abbey's help in resetting all the digital clocks. She must be a lot like me, technology challenged. She lives in a one-bedroom apartment on the 21st floor. Great view. Abbey picked up some clothes. He has been sleeping on the living room sofa since he and Joel split up. Sort of sad.

SUNDAY JUNE 13, 1982

I invited Chrisy for brunch. Since she broke up with my brother Mark, I have tried to stay in touch. I wanted her to meet Abbey. They really connected. After eating we walked around the neighborhood. Towards the East River is a cool old white porcelain-panel fire station with bright red doors. Pure art deco style. I took a series of photos of the three of us posing in front of the doors. We were all in our black leather jackets. The only real color was Abbey's red eyeglass frames and the red doors. I can't wait to see how they turn out. Maybe some material for a new oil painting.

Monday June 14, 1982

On tonight's phone call with Abbey, he told me all about his favorite cousin Judy. She's nine years older, and like me, studied architecture at Cornell. Judy married a Cornell architecture classmate and has two teenage daughters. She lives in a loft on Cornelia Street. When Abbey's extended family gets together for the Jewish holidays they often end up in Judy's loft. Abbey said we'll be celebrating Rosh Hashana there in September. He's already treating me like family.

Tuesday June 15, 1982

It's our two-week anniversary. Abbey had an announcement when he called tonight. He and Shirley both signed up for a nonsmoker's support group run by the American Heart Association. It was Shirley's idea, she heard about it on the evening news. They are offering free clinics. She hopes that if she and Abbey do it together, maybe they can both stop smoking. God, I hope so. I know it's extremely difficult to break the addiction. I'll do whatever I can to support both of them. In the meantime, Abbey never smokes if I'm around. I appreciate that because it really upsets me. Abbey confessed he smokes a pack a day. It breaks my heart. I really wish I could help, but I know this is a battle Abbey has to win on his own.

Wednesday June 16, 1982

Summer is around the corner. After work I went to Paragon Sporting Goods on Broadway to look at their new crop of Speedos. I knew we'd be headed out to Fire Island over the summer and I needed something sexier than my old boxer trunks. Something to keep Abbey's full attention. Afterall, Fire Island is famous for wrecking young couples. I found a great one. Aqua blue, super brief, shows off the equipment nicely.

Thursday June 17, 1982

My second group therapy session with Terrence and the guys.

Steve, the New York University grad student had a great story to share. He's super cute. I find him terribly sexy in his skin-tight torn Levi's. He went to the Saint over the weekend. He's a member and it turns out he knows Jim's new boyfriend Sandy quite well. Small world. Well get this, Sandy introduced Steve to Jim. Not only that, but Jim gave Steve some head in the balcony. I reminded myself of Terrence's strict rule: no sex between group mates. Hands off Steve.

Graham spoke up next. He's the accountant working for a firm on Lower Broadway. He recently came out and is new to New York City. He went to Man's Country for the first time this week, hoping to meet someone he could take out to dinner. The room exploded in laughter. Steve said the guys in Man's Country are only interested in sampling cock, not filet mignon. He suggested Graham might have better success going to Julius'.

Brandon reported that he and his lover Jason were attending a book convention next week in Boston and he will miss group. Jason always tags along. Apparently, Brandon and Jason have done pretty much everything together for eight years.

Eric, the graphic designer, said he and his partner Aaron, who is also a graphic designer working in the same firm, have been under a lot of pressure at work from several younger gays to check-out the backroom at the Stud. They've never been. Eric said Aaron and he both know it's a den of steamy oral sex. It attracts them and frightens them at the same time. Eric and Aaron have been totally monogamous for four years. Eric asked the group for their advice. It was a hard call. Everyone could relate to Eric's question. I told him it didn't have to be all or nothing. They could watch from the side lines. Or they could blow each other off in the middle of the room for all to witness. That could be a very hot declaration of their love and devotion, plus, it might spice up their sex life. That got a round of applause. I hugged Eric.

Terrence asked Darko how his week was going so far. Darko is shy and talks softly. He hardly looks at anyone when he talks. He cut right to the chase. Everyone in the group already knew Darko is a tearoom queen. Apparently, this is what Darko always talks about in group. This week he was in the men's room tearoom in the basement of the main public library on Fifth Avenue. A cute bookish guy showed up and asked Darko if he'd like to blow him. Well, apparently, he did such a masterful job, that the guy gave him his number. Darko asked the group for their advice. Everyone encouraged Darko to call up the book worm, maybe set up a dinner date, but before they ordered dinner, have the guy follow him to the men's room for a blowjob. Then charm the guy during dinner. Maybe suggest your place for dessert. This is some therapy group.

I spoke last. I told them that Abbey and I had only been together for fifteen days, but that they have been the happiest days of my life. I told them that Abbey is forcing me to take it slow, that I only get to sleep with him on Fridays, Saturdays and Sundays; but that's okay, it forces me to work on my "needy" issue. I also told them that when Abbey told his mother to expect both of us for the big family supper in mid-September for Rosh Hashana, that meant Abbey already understands that we will be together for a long time.

Friday June 18, 1982

Tonight, was my first Friday Shabbat dinner at Shirley's. It was my first visit with her. She welcomed me with a wonderful long hug, the same kind of warm hug Abbey gives. I love Shirley. She's relaxed, funny, full of stories. First, she asked all about my family. She wanted to know what it was like being a twin with my sister Melanie. She asked all about my parents. I guess I passed the test. She told me she expected to be seeing a lot more of me. She also mentioned she always walks with Abbey in the New York City Gay Pride Parade. She had it marked in on her wall calendar—Sunday June 27th. I told her I'd be there.

Saturday June 19, 1982

I have a pair of roller skates. They're bright yellow with soft rubber wheels. I bought them shortly after Jim and I broke up. I started skating around the Financial District on weekends when no one was around. I found it very relaxing. I especially enjoy the huge plaza at the World Trade Center with the giant bronze globe in the center. I love the twin towers, so simple and strong, like two giant titans. I surprised Abbey this morning. I gave him his own pair of skates, also bright yellow. Today we skated together for the first time. It was wonderful. After an hour or so, when we were all tired and sweaty, we stopped in the middle of the WTC plaza and lay down on our backs, just looking up at the sky. The beautiful silver towers framed our view, jutting up like giant glaciers in a cobalt blue sea.

SUNDAY JUNE 20, 1982

Angie came down to the loft for dinner to meet Abbey. They really hit it off. That happens all the time with Angie. She is just the most wonderful woman. I made my brother's pasta carbonara. Angie brought baklava, apropos since her roots are Turkish. Afterwards, we walked down to Chase Manhattan Plaza. Years ago, when she worked in the interiors department at SOM, Angie worked on several renovations of the executive floors. Angie confided in me that she's in the running for a Fulbright scholarship to study architecture in India. She's waiting to hear the results. We wished her good luck.

3

SUMMER

MONDAY JUNE 21, 1982

It's the first day of summer.

On our phone call tonight Abbey and I shared our experiences in New York City leather bars, mostly those in the Meat Packing District like the Hellfire Club, the Ramrod and the Anvil. Abbey used to hang out in them with a real S&M leather couple, Fred and Steve. They were actually a couple of pussycats underneath all that leather. They showed Abbey the ropes, shielded him when necessary. Abbey was mostly a voyeur. That part of his life is largely in the past. In contrast, I'm a late bloomer. I've only explored the topic recently, since Jim and I broke up. Jim was never interested. But I always found the butch leather scene a real turn on. A real contrast to drag queen shows. I love my motorcycle jacket, but I don't own a motorcycle and the only time I've ridden one was recently with Jed. I loved that. It was all about freedom.

Abbey suggested he could give me a few guided tours so I can see it all for myself in the flesh. It might destigmatize them a bit, so I can move beyond them. I loved the idea. So on the way home, Abbey took me on a detour through the Hellfire Club. We watched a New York City fireman in a sling being manhandled by a shirtless construction worker in muddy overalls. They were both overacting, but I could tell they were just having fun. It was all a big act. Abbey is becoming my second therapist. What will Terrence say? Abbey told me he has a briefcase full of sex toys from his leather days. I suggested he bring it down to the loft. He can play Master and show me how things work.

TUESDAY JUNE 22, 1982

We had an early breakfast at Black Sheep in the West Village. I've known the owner Michael for years. He's very sexy. He's always been super friendly. I think he has the hots for me. This morning he finally made his move. When I got up to use the men's room he followed me to the urinals, pulled out his dick and jerked himself off while looking at me. I was stunned and more than a bit turned on. Next thing I knew he had his hand on my butt. I figured I better get back to Abbey before I get myself into real trouble. Abbey wasn't surprised. "It's those skin-tight raunchy Levi's you like to wear." He said jokingly he's going to have to keep me on a short leash.

WEDNESDAY JUNE 23, 1982

With all this talk about sex, I figured I should reinstall my fishnet hammock, the one Jim and I used a few times for anal sex. I mentioned it to Abbey on the phone tonight and he's definitely interested. In fact, it's a favorite fantasy of his from porno flicks. He'd definitely like to butt-fuck me in the hammock if I'm up for it. I told him absolutely. We'll have something to look forward to on Friday night.

THURSDAY JUNE 24, 1982

This will be my third group therapy session with Terrence and the gang. I'm really looking forward to it.

Graham was eager to speak. He was all excited. He's been hanging out in Julius' after work all week. He's gotten to know the bartenders and has met half a dozen guys. No sex yet, but he's spoken to a guy named John over

118

the past few nights and is thinking of asking him out on a dinner date next time he sees him. The group gave him the thumbs up.

Eric, the graphic designer, reported that he and his partner Aaron, went to the backroom at the Stud last Saturday night for the first time. It was an eye opener. First, they danced together in a tight embrace in the middle of the crowded backroom. Then they each took turns giving each other blowjobs, making sure nobody cut in. Eric said it was beautiful and that it had helped him get beyond the Stud and fall in love with Aaron all over again. Everyone hugged Eric in a giant group hug.

Darko reported he had called up the book worm, who by the way is named Jerry, and set up a dinner date at his apartment. Darko was stunned when Jerry actually showed up. Darko was straight with Jerry. He told Jerry all he has thought about all week is making love to Jerry's enormous cock. But before he does that again, either there or in some tearoom, he wants to first get to know Jerry a little. Well, what a surprise; they talked for hours. Before Jerry said goodnight, he gladly let Darko feast to his heart's content. They agreed to meet next week at Jerry's place in the Village.

Steve, the cute New York University grad student, reported he had nothing to report. It was a quiet week. He skipped the Saint. He thanked his group mates for their inspiring work this week. He said he was moved by all their stories.

I finished last again. I told them about my long phone call with Abbey about leather bars and Abbey's subsequent guided tour of the Hellfire Club. They particularly enjoyed my report of the New York City fireman in a sling.

Terrence asked me how Abbey's tour compared to my previous solo visits. I told Terrence I have always found leather bars and sex clubs to be very addictive. It's like once I get a taste, I can't get enough. But with Abbey at my side I felt more in control, safer and more protected.

Terrence said good work. "Everybody, remember to play safe."

Friday June 25, 1982

When Abbey walked through the door into the loft tonight, the lights were all off except at the far end where I had carefully positioned a spotlight on the white hammock. Even from the front door forty feet away Abbey could make out my body lying on my back in the hammock, just waiting for him. I was nude except for an old frayed jock strap. Abbey approached silently like in a dance, undressing slowly as he walked towards me one step at a time. He'd drop each garment on the floor until he was naked. He stopped to stroke his gorgeous piece just for me. Abbey spoke to me real slow, nice and dirty, knowing I'd love each word. "I see somebody wants to get butt-fucked really bad, all the way. I better get this butt boy handled, manhandled that is. Where's that sex paddle? Am I right butt boy? Think you can handle it boy?" "Yes Sir."

Saturday June 26, 1982

After that night of raunchy sex in the hammock, I felt totally connected to Abbey. I was his butt boy. He was tremendous. What a lover; his raw lust left me totally drained.

We took a breather and walked over to see the progress on the new South Street Seaport taking shape nearby. It had the feel of New York in the mid-19th century. Several giant old sailing vessels were already docked there. I tried to imagine what it must have been like for two queer sailors back then. Me and Abbey, sailor buddies, secret lovers, sucking away all night in the bed hammocks below deck, butt-fucking behind the wooden barrels on the main deck, then later on, another round out on the open sea, in the moonlight, surrounded by white caps, brazen, half naked, taking turns shooting our wads of hot cum across the rough deck into the choppy sea.

Sunday June 27, 1982

Today is the New York City Gay Pride Parade down Fifth Avenue to Christopher Street. Abbey and I are marching with Shirley behind the PFLAG banner. It stands for Parents, Families & Friends of Lesbians and Gays. Perfect sunny weather. It's my first time actually marching in the

120

parade. Jim and I always watched from the sidewalk. Cowards. It's much better actually marching in the street. You get to see all the wonderful people gathered on the sidewalks; see their facial expressions, staring in disbelief or cheering us on, giving us their love, hope and pride. Walking hand-in-hand between Abbey and Shirley, outdoors in the brilliant sunshine, I felt gay pride for the first time in my life. This marked a key moment of my arrival.

MONDAY JUNE 28, 1982

This evening Shirley came down for dinner. Her first time to the loft. She loved it. The bohemian atmosphere appealed to her romantic side. I cooked my pasta carbonara yet again; I need to branch out in the kitchen. Jim was usually the cook. I think Abbey will take charge soon. I've really fallen in love with him. Our recent hammock sex has set new records. I never dreamed I could experience such deep sexual pleasure.

TUESDAY, JUNE 29, 1982

After work I stopped in at the Christopher Street Bookstore to check out their leather sex slings. The Black owner Franklin remembered me. "Hi Miles. You look terrific! How's that cock ring working out?" "Great. I have a new boyfriend Abbey and we're getting into sling sex." "Sure, I heard the news directly from Abbey. I probably shouldn't tell you, but Abbey stopped in here last week, looking at sex slings. He told me you're driving him crazy. Congratulations! Abbey's a terrific guy. You're both going to love sling sex. It's awesome." Franklin showed me some beautiful vintage ones that have a lot of character. I really liked the idea of a used one, just imagining what sex might have gone on in the past using it. Hot guys lying on their backs, legs in the air getting butt-fucked to kingdom come. I'm going to ask Abbey to take a look at a few with me this weekend.

WEDNESDAY JUNE 30, 1982

I've been very busy in the office; no time even for my diary. My twin sister Melanie and her husband Dan are arriving Friday from Wyoming for a three-night stay around July 4th. I got them a room at the Gramercy Park Hotel. Mel is all excited to meet Abbey. I sent her a photo of Abbey. She told me he's hot. As if I didn't know that. But it was nice to hear anyway. I mentioned the sex shop to her and our interest in buying a sex sling. She said it sounded like a hoot! She's always super-cool.

On this week's phone calls, Abbey and I have been trading stories on the gay disco scene in New York City. I've been filling him in on my trips to the Saint since I broke up with Jim. Abbey hasn't been there yet and expressed interest. I was sure Jim would ask Sandy to get Abbey and me in as his guests. We'll target the Saturday after next.

Abbey loves to dance shirtless on a crowded dance floor working up a good sweat. His favorite disco is an afterhours bar called the Barn in the Meat Packing District near the river. Lots of hot young kids. Abbey said it's friendly, not pretentious. Nothing like the Saint.

THURSDAY JULY 1, 1982

Tonight, was another group therapy session, #4 with Terrence.

Graham went first. His dinner plans with John never panned out. Graham has been wondering if he's going about this the wrong way. He always hears about guys finding quick sex in the backroom at the Stud. So he went there last Sunday late afternoon. He had incredible oral sex in the dark for the first time in his life. He felt so relieved; like he'd finally come out for real. But now he doesn't know what to do next. Most guys in the group thought Graham should go back to Julius', give it another try. Just be friendly, relax, be yourself. Don't keep a score card. Just enjoy the company. See where it leads.

Eric reported that he and Aaron are thinking of taking a full share in a house in the Pines this summer. They both want to explore an open relationship together. They realized that after the Stud experience, they both need to broaden their sexual lives. They are thinking about threesomes where they can share these experiences together in a safe environment. The group was

122

pretty split on this one as you might expect. It's one of the biggest issues facing gay couples. Everyone wished Eric all the best.

Darko reported that he and Jerry spent most of the weekend together, mostly in bed. The sex between them is fantastic, so as long as that lasts, things look good. But Darko also knows it could all vanish in a moment. He's frightened. The group urged Darko to open up to Jerry. Tell him his fears, his aspirations. Be courageous. Put himself on the line. I asked him, what's the worst thing that can happen? You both go back to your tearooms. Darko laughed.

Steve, the hot New York University grad student reported he met somebody in the sex balcony of the Saint. The guy was a total sex animal. Steve never had such intense sex before. When Steve asked him out for dinner the guy said he was too busy. He's a surgeon-in-training with extremely long hours. He told Steve he's only available for quick fuck dates, take it or leave it. Steve told him to leave it. I didn't have the heart to tell Steve I knew the guy. He was Andrei.

Brandon checked in. He and Jason had a good trip to the book conference in Boston. They saw hundreds of new books, plus plenty of cute guys browsing them. Now they are planning their annual trip to London in September. The big question this time is if they will fly first class. Brandon confessed his life sounded so boring compared to the rest of the group. He said he and Jason just go through the motions. The passion is long gone. He misses the messy excitement of lustful desires from his youth. Crazy sex in public settings. His life with Jason is so predictable, so safe, so boring. He is always lusting after cute guys, but never acting, chasing them around, but never taking the candy.

I finished last again. I told Brandon I could easily relate to all his comments. I told him how I lived in a safe closed monogamous relationship for nine years. Just like Brandon and Jason, with annual trips to Europe. Jim and I slowly suffocated each other in spite of our love. It was no one's fault. Love just faded; passions slowly dried up over the years. Meanwhile, new adventures and new lovers, grabbed our attention. Life moved on; we moved with it. Maybe that is the natural course of life; I don't know. I'm starting over again with Abbey; I'm already building the new nest. The new love is thrilling, it overwhelms me. I am utterly powerless to refuse it. I hugged Brandon.

Terrence asked each of us to stop everything for a few minutes this week and love themselves a little bit more.

Friday July 2, 1982

Mel and Dan arrive mid-day from Wyoming. They are staying at the hotel on Gramercy Park. The room is fine. They are leaving Tuesday. Mel already loves Abbey.

Saturday July 3, 1982

Christopher Street was a must see, especially the leathermen showing off their goods. Mel liked flirting with them. Dan took her photo hugging the Black guy Franklin who owns the sex shop. She really enjoyed looking at the merchandise. Franklin, who always wears full leather, started telling her dirty stories about the backroom. It got pretty outrageous. They were both laughing with tears. Then, when Abbey and I started looking at the vintage sex slings, we started laughing as well. We all had a ball. It was healthy getting sex out in the open for a change. On the way out, Franklin gave Mel a warm hug.

Sunday July 4, 1982

The biggest hit was a Szechuan dinner in Chinatown followed by the spectacular Macy's 4th of July fireworks lit from barges on the East River. They filled the entire sky. I love showing off New York City.

MONDAY JULY 5, 1982

Melanie and Dan left exhausted, but happy. Abbey and Mel got a chance to really bond.

TUESDAY JULY 6, 1982

My twin sister Mel really wears me out. She's a public-school art teacher. I guess you need a ton of energy to deal with all those screaming kids. She's nonstop. Her husband Dan is good for her. He's Mr. Cool, always relaxed. He's a high school coach, a real jock, sexy with heavy black eyebrows, I'm sure he's a dynamo in bed.

Abbey had a ball. Mel was all over him. She told Abbey he's hot and easily understood why I fell in love with him. That's Mel. Of course, she also loved Jim. I guess she'll love all the men in my life.

As soon as we sent Mel and Dan off, we went to see Franklin to pick up our new sex sling. We chose the one that looked the most used. The thick black leather seat had turned a faded brown over the years. The ceiling chains and leg straps had a beautiful dull finish. Once lovingly installed back at the loft, Abbey oiled it lightly and polished the seat with a soft white cloth. I tried it out for size. It was a perfect fit. "Is my butt-boy ready?" "At your service Sir. I'm all yours."

WEDNESDAY JULY 7, 1982

I called up Jim. I told him Abbey and I planned to spend a weekend in Cherry Grove at the Belvedere. It's the only place to stay in the Grove. We'd booked a room for July 17th. There is no such thing as a simple room. I knew Jim and Sandy were renting a house in the Grove for two weeks in mid-July, shortly before they leave for San Francisco. Jim insisted on meeting Abbey. I knew Abbey was nervous about the whole idea. Jim suggested we drop by their house for afternoon cocktails on Saturday. Sandy won't be there. I was cautiously optimistic. I would like it if Jim and Abbey could somehow become friends. It would help keep Jim in my life as an important friend. We'd been through too much to just throw it all away.

Thursday July 8, 1982

Another group therapy session tonight with Terrence and the gang. #5. I miss them. I'm bonding with them just like Terrence predicted I would.

Graham told the group that he returned to the backroom of the Stud just once. It was a disaster. The guy he was blowing just walked away in the middle with no explanation. Graham felt completely inadequate. What had he done wrong? So, the next night he went back to Julius' as we suggested. He promised himself he would meet an attractive man and charm him off his feet. Well, it worked. Peter is a stock broker on Wall Street. He's also 32 and has only been in New York City fifteen months. Graham offered to take Peter out for dinner the following night or stay in and let Graham cook his Julia Child's beef bourguignon. Of course, Peter chose the latter. The meal was a hit and the sex before was even better. The group gave Graham a wild round of hoots and hollers. It was great.

Eric reported that he and Aaron have signed up to rent a cottage for the full season on Beach Hill Walk in the Pines. It's behind a much larger four-bedroom house with a pool for eight guys. The cottage has its own private entrance, so Eric and Aaron can bring back tricks, day or night, without having to worry about housemates. Sounds ideal. They've really thought it through. It also sounds like a hot den of sex. The group was jealous. We congratulated Eric on his creative solution and told him we'd be expecting a full report.

Darko told the group that he and Jerry are still together. They talk a lot, mostly about sex. Jerry likes to talk filthy dirty during sex which suits Darko just fine. So, for the time being things are good, but the long-term future looks dubious. Terrence cautioned Darko, either correct his course or expect to be lost at sea shortly. Darko laughed.

Steve met a fellow grad student this week in the main library. Well, actually, it was in the busy library tearoom in the basement. They held each other's cocks briefly at the urinals and then left for a night of nonstop sex in Steve's apartment. His name is Gordon. He's also an economics major. Super cute butt; Gordon loves to get fucked. Steve is a top. He's taking Gordon to the Saint on Saturday. Gordon wants to get butt-fucked by Steve in the balcony. Sounds hot to me. The group urged slowing down a bit, but Steve didn't seem interested in that option at all.

Brandon and Jason booked their first-class airplane tickets to London in September. They are staying at The Savoy. Jason wants to make a side day trip to Cambridge. Brandon is hot to hear the boy choristers in the Choir of King's College. Sounds like something Jim and I would have done.

Seems as if I finished last again. I told Brandon he reminded me of Jim. They both share a deep love of literature and the arts. But when I told him that Jim, the Ivy League professor, basically had a meltdown; that he left me for a younger disco twinkie, Brandon seemed shocked. I just told him to beware, these things happen. Be on guard. Terrence interjected, "Miles, was Jim's leaving you his salvation or was your escape to Venice your seed of rebirth?" "Honestly, I would have to say it was both."

Terrence thanked us all for our good work tonight.

FRIDAY JULY 9, 1982

After work Abbey and I grabbed some sushi and saw Tootsie at the Paris. Dustin Hoffman plays Dorothy who falls for Julie played by Jessica Lange. It's not that complicated. Very cute. Abbey and I both love the Paris theater. The design is based on a circle. Super cool.

SATURDAY JULY 10, 1982

Tonight is the night I take Abbey to the Saint for his first visit. I want it to be perfect. Sandy came through with two guest passes. It opened less than two years ago and is still the hottest gay ticket in town.

After a long morning workout at the Chelsea, we had burgers at Hamburger Harry's off City Hall Park. I always order their vanilla milk shake. By 6 pm we were back in bed with the shades down, ready for a nice long nap. We set the alarm for 1 am, then took our protein drinks and a quick rinse. Heavy pink socks, black work boots, white spandex gym shorts and a white sleeveless Italian tank top. Green bomber jacket. Abbey followed my lead, but he was much more butch, in torn faded 501s, a tight white tee with his black leather vest. Gorgeous. His red glasses were the perfect look. They'll think he's from the Warhol Factory in Union Square. I called for a taxi to Second Avenue in the East Village. I needed my ear plugs; the music was loud. Abbey's tough; he could take it. He grabbed my hand and we were suddenly shirtless in the middle of the dance floor, jumping to the beat of Donna Summer, surrounded by a sweaty brotherhood of gym bods. Gay heaven. As the giant central star machine rose out of the floor, everyone cheered the universe of stars.

We passed on the balcony. What was the point? We'd be much happier at home in our new sling. We did sign up for the sunrise blueberry pancakes at the all-night diner around the corner. A line of yellow taxi cabs was waiting outside to take the wasted party boys home. Safe back in the loft, we spent all of Sunday in bed, Abbey in my arms. It was lovely, magical, like no other night ever. Abbey's last words before falling asleep were, "My ears are ringing. Donna Summer is singing inside my head."

SUNDAY JULY 11, 1982

By Sunday afternoon we had totally recovered from the Saint. We both craved sushi and a trip to Man's Country. It was hopping. In the lounge Abbey started talking to Tex. He really was a Texas cowboy. In New York City on his first visit ever, hoping to score big on sex, hetero or homo. We started petting him, mussing with his dirty blond hair, getting him to laugh a little. He was in full cowboy drag, boots and all. Cute as can be. Talked with a Texas drawl. He had the hots for me in my Levi's. He kept squeezing my butt. We invited him back to our room upstairs. "Let's give you the full New York City welcome. How about a nice piece of ass, maybe a proper butt-fuck? Bet you haven't gotten much of that back in Dallas. What do you think Cowboy?"

128

MONDAY JULY 12, 1982

Billy called me at the office early Monday morning. He sounded very excited. I hadn't spoken to him since our meeting at GMHC. He wants to see me for lunch. He proposed meeting at the Paley Park Café at 53rd Street at eleven. Billy knows I love the space. It's a tiny pocket park tucked between tall skyscrapers. The cascading waterfall is great. I often come here to read on my lunch hour.

When Billy suddenly appeared in his leather motorcycle jacket I knew something big was up; he looked radiant. I sensed immediately that he was in love. I gave him my warmest hug. "How's it going buddy? You look magnificent." He was so excited he could hardly speak.

"Last Friday night I finally broke down. I got out all my old leather drag and went back to the Spike. It's been years. I fell back into my old routine in the backroom. I used to call it S&M, "Standing and Modelling." I was always a pro at it. Super-hot on the surface, but frozen and dead underneath. My loneliness I numbed with drugs. Last Friday night was so different. I found my old comrade Jeremy. He looked completely alive. I touched his gentle face. God was he gorgeous. He looked wiser. He wrapped me in an embrace that left me breathless. We both started crying. We started making love standing in the middle of the room; shedding our leather shields, piece-by-piece, until we were both naked. His eyes locked onto mine. We adored each other's bodies, two worn tired men starving for love. Jeremy rescued me. I rescued Jeremy."

We spent the whole weekend together, mostly in bed making love and talking about everything. I've never felt this way about anyone before. I'm so happy." Billy broke into tears. We hugged as I rubbed his thick blond hair. "Dear Billy, you deserve this." I laughed and hugged him again. "Yes, Billy, I look forward to meeting this gorgeous stud of yours named Jeremy! Wow! Once you two love birds settle down, we'll all get together with Abbey. Meanwhile, God bless you both."

Tuesday July 13, 1982

I gave Abbey the good news about Billy and Jeremy. I suggested Abbey show me the Spike after midnight. Sort of an indirect way for us to connect to Billy and Jeremy until we can all get together in person. I'd never been there before. It's on 11th Avenue at 20th Street by the West Side Highway. It has a masculine feel. Leather and Levi's. Lots of hot men in black. I can see why Billy likes to hang out there. With his shaved head, he'd fit right in. Later on, Billy told me, he and Jeremy have decided to say farewell to the Spike. It's in their shared pasts now. It's time to move on.

Wednesday July 14, 1982

On tonight's long phone call with Abbey, he told me the wonderful story of how his middle sister Susie forced Abbey to come out to his parents about ten years ago. Abbey was twenty-years-old and totally closeted at the time, living at home on the Upper East Side with his parents before their divorce. Susie was living in a hippie commune in Eugene, Oregon. She came to visit for the weekend. Shortly before dinner she came into Abbey's room and closed the door. "I think you should tell mommy and daddy that you're gay." Abbey responded in shock. "How do you know I'm gay?" "It's pretty obvious. I've known for some time." Abbey said he didn't think it was a good idea. Susie responded, "If you don't tell them, I will, and I'm going back to Eugene tomorrow morning." Meanwhile, Eddie ordered take out Chinese food. The four of them sat down at the dinner table. Abbey was looking at Susie, Susie was looking at Abbey. Conversation was awkward. Susie spoke first.

"Well, Abbey, don't you have something to say." Abbey responded, "Can't we wait until after the dessert." Four fortune cookies were passed around, as was the family custom. Shirley read hers aloud first. "A gay time is in store for all." Abbey practically fell off his chair as Susie started laughing hysterically. Shortly thereafter, Abbey said, "I have an announcement to make." Abbey then opened up and spoke nonstop for twenty minutes, as if he was giving a college lecture, filling them in on all the details of his hidden life—joining Gay Activists Alliance, volunteering at New York Gay Switchboard, his first boyfriend Donald and so much more. When he finally stopped exhausted, there was an awkward silence. Abbey spoke first.

"So, well? Do you have any questions? Are you surprised?" Shirley said no; Eddie remained silent.

THURSDAY JULY 15, 1982

Tonight is already my 6th group therapy session with Terrence. I'm really starting to feel close to these guys. I'm also starting to feel like my issues are pretty small compared to some of theirs.

Graham and Peter are seeing each other this weekend. They reserved a room at the Plaza as a romantic New York City mini-vacation. Peter wants to have dinner at the Rainbow Room.

Eric and Aaron spent their first weekend in their cottage in the Pines. It was pretty wild. They picked up a cute kid in the Meat Rack Saturday night. The kid blew Aaron back at the cottage and then disappeared into the main house next door. Sunday morning Eric spotted him lounging around the pool with another trick. The group laughed, "Welcome to the Pines."

Terrence asked Eric how he felt about it. Eric confessed he was upset with Aaron, as if Aaron had somehow abandoned him for the kid. He said he should have seen it coming and was disappointed with himself. The group urged Eric to talk it through with Aaron. Tell him how much he loves him. Maybe put the Meat Rack on the back burner for a while. Try low tea at the Botel. It's casual, friendly, less of a sex auction. Maybe it's time to meet a new guy as a friend, not as a lover.

Darko told the group that he and Jerry split up. It happened when Jerry suggested he and Darko check out the subway tearoom at the IRT #1 at Bloomingdale's. Darko actually was fine with the plan, he kind of missed the toilets. They both scored and left separately with horny guys. The group was stunned. Steve called Darko a "tearoom slut." Terrence asked Steve to apologize to Darko, which he did. Terrence then asked Darko if he intended to go back to his tearoom routine. Darko said "Yes, I do. I don't have a choice."

Steve declared he is already falling for Gordon. They did the Saint balcony on Saturday night and then spent all of Sunday fucking in Steve's bed at home. Gordon is Steve's perfect butt- boy. He's driving Steve crazy. The group suggested Steve plan something that doesn't involve anal sex, like a museum, a movie, a walk across the Brooklyn Bridge. Get to know the other side of Gordon a little. Let things cool off a bit. Sure, still have some hot fun, but mix things up a bit. Steve thanked us.

Brandon told the group he had been thinking a lot about what I said to him last week concerning Jim's meltdown. I really hit a raw nerve. First, he thanked me. Then he shocked us all by saying that he has proposed a trial separation from Jason after eight years together. Jason was initially stunned, but within a few days he agreed it made sense to try. They set a window of six months. That would give each of them enough time to figure out what they really wanted long-term. The news left the group in the dumps. What a surprise. I felt especially bad, as if I brought it all on. Terrence hugged Brandon and pledged the support of the group. He asked Brandon to share all his feelings in this safe space and reminded Brandon that we loved him.

I finished the session again. I told Brandon that he reminded me of myself. I told him that after Jim left, I reached out to him to remain close friends. After nine years together, we had shared too much to not be connected. Brandon understood and hugged me.

FRIDAY JULY 16, 1982

Abbey and I left work early to catch the train to Sayville, Long Island. We're headed to Cherry Grove for a two-night stay at the Belvedere which is owned by an ex-model of a pencil fortune. There is no such thing as a simple room. Ours had a four-poster bed with plenty of fluff everywhere. Not our taste, but it will have to do; after all, we are in Cherry Grove. We had a good seafood dinner in town at the Monster. Afterwards, a moonlit walk on the beach.

Saturday July 17, 1982

We discovered, much to our surprise, that the hotel pool, which was so prominently featured in the ad, was off limits to the hotel guests. It was only for the owner. This fact was concealed at check-in. We spent the morning on the beach, walking over to the Pines. While the Grove is primarily made up of modest beach shacks from the 50s, the Pines is a collection of more recent architectural wonders, many of which are quite grand and beautiful. On our next visit, we agreed, we will most likely be staying in the Pines.

Our afternoon was booked. Jim was expecting us for cocktails at the house he and Sandy rented for two weeks. It was one of the few tasteful houses in the Grove. Jim answered the door, greeting Abbey and I warmly, a Bloody Mary in his hand. Jim immediately handed us similar drinks. Jim had made sure Sandy was not around. Abbey whispered in my ear. "I think he plans to poison me." Jim soon had Abbey charmed. That was Jim, the charmer. He and Abbey bonded quickly. Lots of talk about the Saint, one of the few things we had in common. That, and San Francisco, where Abbey had lived for five months in the early 70s. In just thirteen days Jim and Sandy would be off to the Castro in their U-Haul rental. Parting was bittersweet. Soon the man I'd spent every day with for nine years would walk out of my life. It still felt odd.

Sunday July 18, 1982

Billy called Sunday morning. Yesterday he and Jeremy moved into their own apartment in Brooklyn Heights on Henry Street. Jeremy really wants to meet me and Billy really wants to meet Abbey. So Abbey and I are invited over to their new apartment for a simple dinner tonight. It will be their first-time cooking in the kitchen.

Billy and Jeremy make a terrific couple. They are both so sexy and totally bonkers in love. It's beautiful. They just can't stop touching each other all over. It's really cute. Jeremy is 40. He's bald like our Billy. He's super butch. I can see why Billy fell for him. He looks like a hot Colt model. He's a city planner in the Mayor's office. He simply adores Billy. He must have thanked me three times for "saving" Billy. After dinner, Billy had a special gift for Abbey. It was in a small robin egg blue Tiffany & Co. box. Inside was a plain silver men's bracelet with a single inset diamond. Inscribed in a continuous string on the inside, it read ....for Abbey, who loves Miles, who loves Billy, who loves Jeremy, who loves Abbey, ...

MONDAY JULY 19, 1982

All day long I've been thinking about Abbey's new bracelet from Billy and the poignant inscription. I'm so touched Billy reached out to Abbey. Billy wisely understands Abbey is the center of my life, just like Jeremy is the center of his. We all love and respect each other. It really is a brotherhood of gay men. Each of us has the other's back.

TUESDAY JULY 20, 1982

On the phone call tonight with Abbey, I discovered something interesting. West Orange, New Jersey in the Borscht Belt was a weekend 50s getaway for Abbey growing up. It was popular with young Jewish couples from New York City. It turns out Abbey was conceived at Goldman Hotel. Shirley and Eddie were busy screwing there one spring day, making my sweetheart Abbey. Not only that, their favorite assigned waiter in the main dining room was named Abbey. They adored him. When baby Abbey was finally born nine months later, he was legally named Abe, after Shirley's Uncle Abe, the man who got jobs for the entire family during the Depression. The only problem was Shirley didn't like the name, so she decided to give him the nickname Abbey after her favorite Goldman waiter. It stuck. Abe always asks people to call him Abbey.

WEDNESDAY JULY 21, 1982

On tonight's phone call with Abbey, I told him all about my evening with Jack at the Mine Shaft. Abbey really surprised me when he revealed he knew Jack from the early days of Gay Activists Alliance. Not only that, Abbey had a foursome with Jack and the S&M leather couple Abbey knows, Fred and Steve, way back when. Wow, I was blown away! Here I'm going on to Abbey about Jack, while Abbey had sex with the man a decade earlier! I felt sort of foolish. Abbey was nice about it; he didn't rub it in.

Thursday July 22, 1982

Tonight was my group therapy session #7 with Terrence and the gang. It seems like the guys are settling down a bit.

Graham and Peter's big weekend date at the Plaza was a big hit. They changed their plans for the Rainbow Room. Ended up with simple burgers at Hamburger Harry's and a romantic night visit to the observation deck at the Empire State Building. City lights. More fun and they saved a fortune.

Eric and Aaron decided to spend their second weekend together in their Pines cottage, just the two of them. They had a lovely grilled swordfish steak supper at home. The sex between them all weekend was particularly frequent and hot. Eric thinks it's just from being in such close proximity to all those Pines men. The group definitely agreed.

Darko told the group that he's been staying home, mostly reading and watching porno. He can't decide if he should call up Jerry and ask him over for dinner. He knows he's really waiting for Jerry to make the first move. The group encouraged Darko to give Jerry a second chance. It's a big deal to stop tearoom sex cold turkey. Cut Jerry a little slack. Darko thanked the group for their support.

Steve said he and Gordon have started running long-distance together, from New York University south around Battery Park and back, times two. And he's put the Saint on hold for a month. He finds he's more relaxed, more engaged in conversations with Gordon. Their sex is still in the stratosphere. Gordon is interested in installing a sex sling in Steve's living room. Steve likes the idea. It will be his treat, a gift for his gorgeous butt-boy. The group gave Steve a round of applause and a group hug.

Brandon reported that he has a colleague at work who is out of the country for nine months. He offered to let Brandon use his one-bedroom apartment if he splits the rent. The apartment is at One Christopher Street on a high floor. Brandon plans to move in this weekend. Jason will give him a hand. Brandon is nervously excited. The trial separation is obviously a big deal for both of them.

I told the group that Abbey and I were taking Amtrack to Providence tomorrow after work to see my family. It will be Abbey's introduction to my parents and my sister and brother-in-law. I told them I was nervous. My parents are nothing like Abbey's mother Shirley. They are more than a bit uptight. But I reminded myself they did treat Jim well. Of course, Jim went to Princeton like my brother Mark. That didn't go unnoticed. Would they hold it against Abbey that he's a college drop out? Probably. I don't want them to prejudge Abbey's potential. The group said I should relax; they all felt Abbey had polished social skills to meet my family. Let Abbey charm them like he charmed me. They were absolutely right. I thanked them. Terrence gave me a hug.

MONDAY JULY 23-26, 1982

Our three-day trip to Providence was a great success. All my worries were misplaced. Abbey's genuine warmth indeed carried the day. Abbey and Terry bonded much better than Jim ever had. He got her to laugh a lot.

My parents were as happy as I've ever seen them, despite the fact that Edward was fighting cancer. They were living in a new beautiful ranch home in a lush country setting outside Saunderstown. Edward never complained about a thing. He was warm and generous with Abbey and me. It was a sad time, but I sensed he understood the love that Abbey and I already shared. He respected us as a couple. Abbey made things easier and tried to comfort Terry who was under a lot of stress. I enjoyed doing simple things like yard work with Edward.

My sister and her husband hosted a lasagna dinner at their home. We all enjoyed the visit to the RISD Art Museum. The last night we had a wonderful fish dinner at The Lobster Pot watching the giant waves break. Back home we all played Scrabble in two teams, three players each. Abbey made sure Terry won, so she was happy.

All in all, it was a wonderful visit. On the late Sunday afternoon train back to New York City, I felt how different my life was from theirs. But that was not a problem. I knew we all shared an appreciation of beauty and honesty, in all its forms. We loved and respected each other. That was all that really mattered. I was content with my family and my darling Abbey at my side.

TUESDAY JULY 27, 1982

Abbey told me all about the EST Training on our phone call tonight. He did it a few months ago. His ex-boyfriend Joel had done it before Abbey and recommended it to him. It came out of San Francisco in 1971 by the founder Werner Erhard. It's a series of workshops that is supposed to transform your life, "infuse it with new possibilities." Sounded a little flaky. It consisted of two weekend-long workshops with evening sessions during the week. 200 people at a time. Not cheap. 9:00 am to midnight, one meal-break, no clocks or watches, no note taking, speak only when called upon and strict bathroom breaks. Just imagine if you got caught having sex with a co-participant in the men's room. They'd probably cut your dick off. Actually, no kidding, Abbey said he got a lot out of it. Shirley did it after Abbey. So maybe I'll do it as well. Maybe after Labor Day. I'm still a little skeptical.

WEDNESDAY JULY 28, 1982

I poked into Brooks Brothers over lunch hour to look at the latest fall suits on the second floor; I need another suit for SOM. In the back fitting room, I stumbled on a very cute salesman hanging out inside the last cubicle with the curtain half drawn. He was playing with himself. He saw me smile and waved me in. It all happened so fast. He gave me a terrific blowjob; what a mouth on this kid, a pro. We didn't speak. I was out of there in less than a few minutes.

Back at the office, I mentioned it to Bob. He said he's had oral sex there more than once as well. Once a hot Hispanic salesman even followed him into a cubicle and butt-fucked him with his trousers up. Bob said it was tremendous. You'd never figure this at Brooks Brothers, clothier to the

Hamptons crowd. I don't know if I should tell Abbey. I feel like I have to. I don't ever want to lie to him or deceive him. That would be a huge mistake.

On the phone call tonight with Abbey, I immediately confessed the whole Brooks Brothers saga. Abbey was totally cool. No problem. He said just be careful no guards are around and be sure to watch your wallet. Then he told me my confession had made him rock hard. So, we had our first phone sex. Lots of dirty talk. I loved it. It was better than the blowjob in BB.

THURSDAY JULY 29, 1982

Tonight was my 8th group therapy session with Terrence and my new buddies. I've really bonded with all of them. I really care about them.

Graham and Peter had a quiet week, staying in mostly, renting a few movies, Chinese takeout, plenty of sex. Graham brought up the question of living together. Graham is eager to give it a try. Peter would like to hold off for a few months. One step at a time. Make sure the relationship has a good foundation beyond sex. Graham said fine, he said he could wait for Peter for as long as it takes. He's already sure Peter is the love of his life.

Saturday afternoon Eric and Aaron were picked up by a hot German couple in the Pines Harbor, Hans and Otto. The Germans were looking for a foursome, specifically with two well-hung Americans. When Eric and Aaron dropped their trunks for an inspection, the Germans brought them back to their overgrown bungalow on Neptune. A sex sling was already waiting in the living room. You can imagine the rest. By the time Eric and Aaron returned to their cottage on Sunday late afternoon it was time to head back to the city. Terrence asked "Were you and Aaron pleased with how the weekend turned out?" "Yes and no. It was certainly a shared adventure. But what comes next? That's the big question, isn't it?" "Yes, indeed."

Darko finally got a phone call from Jerry. Jerry proposed a date with Darko at the baths—Man's Country! The group broke out laughing. Jerry was serious; he and Darko shared a room. They had sex together and then cruised around looking for someone to add as a threesome. It's not that uncommon. They actually had a good time. Jerry thought it was a step up from the subway tearooms. The group didn't know what to think. Terrence suggested Darko invite Jerry over for dinner again.

As predicted, Steve installed a sex sling in his living room. Now after their long runs together, they hit the sling. They are both smart enough to know it's nuts, but they are both extremely happy for the time being. The group wished them all the best and gave Steve a group hug.

Brandon had already settled into his new apartment at One Christopher Street. He spent hours looking out the window at the street life below— especially the butch leather couples and the street hustlers. One blond lanky kid in leather has his attention. Given his pose, he must be for sale. Brandon went down to street level to check him out. Up close, the kid had beard stubble and a pierced earing. Brandon smiled, but he hasn't spoken to the kid yet. He's all nervous. The kid smiled back. Brandon said he hadn't given Jason a thought all week. Terrence asked Brandon if he planned to pick up the street hustler? Brandon's quick response was: "It sure looks like it."

I told the group that Abbey and I were made welcome in Providence. All my worries were misplaced. We will visit again in the fall, maybe for my birthday in October.

I also told the group about my surprise sex adventure in Brooks Brothers and how Abbey took it in so easily. The group agreed with Abbey's response, be careful, but enjoy a little fun.

Terrence gave me my usual hug.

Friday July 30, 1982

Jim called very early. It was still dark out. He woke us up in bed. He and Sandy were about to hit the road. Good luck with the U-Haul. The big adventure in San Francisco begins. He called to wish us well. That was nice. I also wished him the best. After I hung up, I kissed Abbey and mussed his hair.

Saturday July 31, 1982

I finally got around to asking Jack to forgive me. I had really hurt him over the age issue at the Mine Shaft last spring. Gays are too often disrespectful of their elders. We'll all be old one day, if AIDS doesn't take us sooner. The truth is Jack and I really have a lot in common and we really enjoy each other's company. When Jack told me that he and Wolf were talking about living together, I was thrilled. Apparently, Wolf has already half moved into One Christopher Street. I adore Wolf. He's always treated me like a gentleman, from that first encounter in the WSS steam room, through all our good times together with Tim. I was proud that I was the one who matched up Jack with Wolf last April at Jack's little dinner party. They'll make a hot biracial couple.

Abbey and I asked Jack and Wolf over for dinner tonight in the loft. Jack and Abbey told hilarious stories from their GAA days and even more hilarious stories from their brief love affair years ago. Jack confessed Abbey was the lover who got away. I really enjoyed seeing them talking together; I love them both. Wolf and Abbey also had a shared past at New York Gay Switchboard, where they both volunteered years ago. I totally surprised Jack and Abbey when I confessed to the steamy butt-fuck I thoroughly enjoyed from Wolf back in February at the WSS.

Jack and Wolf invited us out to the Pines. They are renting a house for all of August. We'll go out the last weekend of the month. That should be fun. On the way out, Jack caught me staring at the obvious, Wolf's massive Black cock pressed tight against his grey sweat pants. I recalled it fondly from last winter. I had been fixated on it all evening. Jack smiled, pulled me aside and whispered. "Maybe when you come out to the Pines we can all

140

have a little reunion in the hot tub." When I told Abbey later he said these guys really know how to have fun.

SUNDAY AUGUST 1, 1982

I had a pair of tickets to the New York City Ballet in Lincoln Center for tonight. They were the last tickets from Jim and my season subscriptions. Jim loved the ballet. We carried subscriptions for years. Jim taught me all about the dancers and George Balanchine. I also like the building they call home, designed by Philip Johnson, the New York State Theater. I loved watching the male dancers in their white tights.

Of course, Abbey joined me. It was his first time at the New York City Ballet. We had dinner before at Café Luxembourg on Amsterdam. Abbey ran into his old buddies Fred and Steve, the cool S&M leather couple, who frequent the ballet. They wore their full leather drag, even leather cod pieces. It was quite a sight during intermission. It shook up some of the old ladies. Afterwards, the four of us agreed to hit the backroom at the Stud and get our rocks off.

MONDAY AUGUST 2, 1982

Abbey called at 7:00 sharp. His deep voice still makes my head buzz. I just lie back in the bed and close my eyes. It doesn't matter what he says; I just enjoy the buzz. It always leaves me hard. He had quite the story tonight. His birthday is August 15th. Last year Joel gave Abbey a special present. They were in the Rawhide in Hell's Kitchen the day before his birthday when this hot young kid walked in. He immediately put the make on Abbey. He practically pounced on him at the bar. Abbey was flattered, but nothing happened. Well, the next day on his birthday, Joel took Abbey back to the Rawhide for a drink. "Abbey, are you ready for your birthday present?" He motioned with a raised hand. The hot kid reappeared. They went back to Joel's apartment. Both Joel and the kid were tied up with ropes as Abbey's sex slaves for the night. He took turns fucking them back and forth for hours. He said it was the most intense sex he's ever had. The kid just couldn't get enough.

TUESDAY AUGUST 3, 1982

After Abbey's sex story last night, I figured it was time to come clean and tell him about my backroom adventure in the Christopher Street Bookstore. It was shortly after Jim left. A clear moonlit night. A gay bus tour group from the Midwest pulled up at midnight with a busload of horny gay tourists. They had just come from Times Square where they had seen a couple of gay striptease acts. I had no idea these things go on most every night. At the Christopher Street Bookstore there was a run on dildoes and sex toys. I met a cute kid from Kansas. I asked if he'd like to blow me in the backroom. He said sure. He was awesome; turned out he was also hung like a horse. I had him fuck me. It was wild. Franklin's shop was swamped for twenty minutes. Outside the sex shop on West Street they vanished as fast as they had arrived. Slowly the shop returned to normal, just quiet horny locals out for some late-night fun. On my way out, Franklin asked me how the new cock ring was working out. "Abbey loves it."

WEDNESDAY AUGUST 4, 1982

Simon called to thank me. He got the job at Der Scutt. He'll be working on a new hotel in Houston. He wants to take me and Abbey out for a thank you dinner after work tonight. He suggested the Mexican restaurant near the Stud. Afterwards he thought we might enjoy the Stud's backroom. We took a rain check on the backroom. We were just there a few days ago with Fred and Steve. Enough is enough.

THURSDAY AUGUST 5, 1982

Tonight is already my 9th group therapy session. Time really flies. I'm looking forward to the guys and to Terrence. I really love Terrence.

Graham and Peter decided quite suddenly to take a half share in a rental house in the Pines. Peter knows a gay couple through work who are looking to split their full share. It's in a four-bedroom house on Beach Hill with a pool. Peter loves the ocean and Graham sees it as an opportunity to meet new people. This coming weekend will be their first. They are nervously excited. Who knows if they will fit in with the other six housemates?

Eric is suddenly all animated. He just put it together. The house Graham just talked about is the main house in front of the cottage he and Aaron have rented for the season. He's a little nervous that he and Aaron's sex antics will end up in group therapy. Imagine if they pick somebody up in the Meat Rack, bring them back to the cottage for hot raunchy sex, and Graham and Peter hear or see them while they're in the pool? Terrence jumps in. "Time out! Let's not get ahead of ourselves. First of all, don't assume your debauchery interests anyone. Secondly, so what if it does? That is the nature of the Pines. Sex is everywhere. If you can't handle that, you shouldn't be there. Just relax." I'd never seen Terrence speak so forcefully. He was great!

Darko followed Terrence's advice and had Jerry over for dinner again. But this time, instead of serving Julia Child's beef bourguignon, he served a hot enchilada from the gay escort service. The group broke out laughing hysterically. Darko was serious. He figured Jerry wanted hot young cock, so he'd give it to him. Darko admitted he's in love with Jerry and just wants to please him. The three of them had sex together and Jerry left extremely pleased with Darko. The group was speechless. Terrence said this was a first ever in his group therapy.

Steve and Gordon are starting to behave like a couple. Gordon moved in. He sleeps over regularly. They still run together daily. The sling sex has tapered off a bit to just once a week. They're both happy. They're also taking a partial share in the Pines this summer. Gordon knows an old leather couple who rent out their beach shack on Neptune. The selling feature that grabbed Steve's attention was the sex sling in the living room with a pair of black leather sofas for voyeurs. The group wished them all the best. This all sounded vaguely familiar.

Brandon took the plunge this week. He spoke to the blond lanky kid outside his window down on Christopher Street. He first offered to buy the kid a cup of soup and a coffee. The kid's blunt response surprised Brandon. "$100 an hour and I'll do anything, take it or leave it." Brandon did a quick calculation in his head and replied: "I'll take $200 please." When the two hours were up, Brandon tipped him $50. He offered to share the bed, no touching, if the kid needed a place to crash. The kid declined the offer and from the door on the way out said, "Hey, old man, you know where to find me." Terrence asked Brandon "How did that make you feel?" "Actually, it felt wonderful. That was the kid's way of saying he wanted to see me again. Yes, wonderful."

I told the group about Simon's invite to the backroom at the Stud. It was to be a thank you for helping him land his new job. We took a raincheck. Abbey and I are taking a break from the Stud.

Terrance asked me why now? I told him we both felt the urge to reconnect lately. A little too much fooling around outside our relationship. We don't need it. We're completely in love. Terrence congratulated me with a hug.

FRIDAY AUGUST 6, 1982

Remember the sugar daddy from the Saint? Robert. Well, he called out of the blue. We had a 4-day fling last March before Abbey. He sounded great. He's planning to build a new beach house in P-town. Do I want to be his architect? You bet! We have similar taste, so it should go smoothly. I can do it on the side at SOM. He'll send me a site plan and photos. I asked him to give me a single-page list of everything he wants in the house. Architects call it the space program.

I told him all about Abbey and how they must meet sometime soon. He congratulated me. "Abbey is a lucky man!"

SUNDAY AUGUST 7-8, 1982

Abbey and I felt like a little escape from New York City. A weekend road trip to Long Island, Abbey's past. Something new. First stop was Great Neck where Abbey grew up. We spent a night at the Bayberry Inn with a seafood dinner. It was like stepping into the past. Childhood houses, an impressive high school campus, an historic town core, a modernist synagogue, the sunken train station to muffle the noise. All in all, pretty cool, clearly a progressive community, a privileged past. Further out a drive-by tour of the campus of Southampton College of Long Island University where Abbey spent a year. A walk along the beach. Snooping around several famous modernist houses. Ridiculously tall clipped hedges to separate the private estates.

MONDAY AUGUST 9, 1982

Jed called me at SOM. It was great to hear his voice again. I immediately recalled our motorcycle ride together, my arms tight around his torso, my nose in his thick black hair. I hadn't heard from him in over two months. That was just before I met Abbey. First thing I asked him about was Max. Jed sounded upset. He started crying. He told me Max is in the hospital with Stage 1 melanoma. He's worried it will kill Max. I told Jed we needed to talk. He'll come down to the loft tomorrow. Abbey asked if he could join us. His uncle is an oncologist at Memorial Sloan Kettering. Abbey will chat with him during the day to get some facts. Abbey knows a lot about medicine and wants to help.

TUESDAY AUGUST 10, 1982

Jed and Abbey bonded immediately. Jed was so impressed at Abbey's interest in Max. Abbey explained to Jed that melanoma is treatable with radiation, especially if it is caught early, as appears to be the case with Max. Jed started crying as Abbey spoke about Max. They hugged and Abbey suggested we all go to the hospital tomorrow after work to cheer up Max.

WEDNESDAY AUGUST 11, 1982

When we all walked into Max's private room, we watched as a huge smile filled his tired face, and tears welled up in his brown eyes. Jed literally jumped into the bed and wrapped his arms around Max's head. He kissed his shiny bald spot over and over. It was almost embarrassing to intrude into their tender private world. Max was so appreciative that we were helping Jed get through this crisis. Max promised to surprise us with something special when this was all over. Jed asked the night nurse if he could sleep the night in the side chair. He wanted to be near Max. They made such a beautiful couple, each so different, one so fragile in youth, the other frail in late middle-age. Jed's spark of life was contagious. Abbey and I left more in love than ever.

THURSDAY AUGUST 12, 1982

It's already my 10th group therapy session with Terrence and the guys. Time is really flying. I've been doing this diary thing forever. Almost eight months. And Abbey has his 31st birthday in just three days. I have to find something special for him.

Graham and Peter had their first Pines weekend. It left them both exhausted. Dinner Friday night started at midnight. They already have a close housemate friend named Trevor; he's a geriatric psychiatrist. The whole house went dancing together at the Pines Pavilion after dinner. It was great, but Graham and Peter both need a weekend to recover from their Pines weekend. They agreed that a half share was plenty. They couldn't imagine what a full share would be like.

Eric said he and Aaron decided they will alternate weekend sex activities to work around Graham and Peter's half share. When Graham and Peter are away, they can go wild, when Graham and Peter are in the Pines, they cool it. Terrence suggested a raised red flag, denoting passion, for when Graham and Peter are away; or a raised white flag, denoting chastity, for when Graham and Aaron are in residence. So, this past weekend Eric and Aaron kept their jeans buttoned up. It was sort of romantic for a change.

Darko reported that Jerry wants to continue renting hustlers for spicy threesomes. They did that on Saturday night and it went smoothly enough. Only the $200 bill at the end was a bit of a shock. In contrast, Terrence noted tearoom sex is largely a free transaction. He jokingly suggested Darko consult with his CPA. I think Darko's days in the group may be numbered. Terrence did not look pleased.

Steve and Gordon are in love with their beach shack on Neptune. Steve described the place for the group—the smell of leather, the vintage porno collection, the well-used sex toys and old jock straps hidden away in drawers, the piles of back issues of Drummer, their pages now stiff from dried cum. Steve and Gordon have taken to long morning runs along the beach, Water Island and beyond. They have already discovered the thrill of outdoor sex in the dunes.

Brandon was feeling a little foolish. He's almost 34, his partner Jason is nearly 42. What's he doing chasing after 20-year-old street hustlers? It's pathetic. But he can't help himself. As a children's book editor, he can work from home, but the distractions out the window are making that impossible. He spoke to the blond lanky kid again; his name is Larry. He noticed that Larry keeps a dark blue bandana in his back right pocket. Brandon asked him what it means. "Doesn't the color and pocket stand for something? I'm too out of it to even know." "Look Brandon, it lets people know I like to butt-fuck guys, get it?" "Actually, I remember that now that you say it. I really enjoyed that part of our sex the most." "Well, you should know, you have a beautiful butt, the kind of butt gay guys go nuts over. You really should show it off more, buy tight spandex gym shorts and start wearing a dark blue bandana in your rear left pocket. I bet you'll see guys following you home." Brandon asked one more question. "Is there a bandana that lets guys know I want to suck them off?" Larry lit up, "Sure, a light blue one in your rear right pocket." "Thanks for the sex lesson Larry. Next time I walk down Christopher Street I'm going to pick up some bandanas from the sex shop. Brandon had the whole group rolling on the floor. Terrence gave Brandon a hug.

I told the group about Max and Jed, their devotion to each other, despite the large age difference, 52 and 26. But I said it wasn't for me. I like the fact that Abbey and I are the same age, we have a shared past. We face life's challenges at the same time, together. Jim was a generation older. While Abbey was at the Stonewall Riots, breaking down doors, Jim was on the sidewalk, watching the television report on the evening news.

Monday August 16, 1982

I finally realized what to get Abbey for his 31st birthday on Sunday—a weekend in the Pines, in our own house, on the front row facing the ocean. I called up the realtor Bob Howard, and he had the perfect house for us, small, modern, right on the ocean, not too far from town for shopping. We would check in Friday at noon and depart Sunday late afternoon.

It's high season already. Our rental house was comfortable. After we settled in, we put on our new Speedos and hit the beach. Cute Pines men everywhere.

We walked around the Co-ops and talked about what it would be like to own our own apartment there. Abbey grilled salmon steaks for dinner. He's a serious griller. After dark we walked around the harbor. The disco was just starting up. We peeked inside. We'll be asleep long before it really gets going.

In darkness early Sunday morning we started out to Water Island in our Speedos. The sunrise was beautiful. The beach was deserted. I recalled what Steve told the group last week; about guys from the Pines having sex in the dunes. I grabbed Abbey's shoulder and started kissing him, my hands mussing his hair, then down inside his trunks. "Let's make love in the sand dunes for your birthday." "Everything for you Miles." Actually, I had it all planned out in advance. The beach towel, the tiny tube of KY, the sunscreen for afterwards, a bottled water. We took turns. It was a perfect birthday weekend.

Tuesday August 17, 1982

Angie called me in the morning at work. She wants to host a surprise belated birthday party tonight for Abbey in her apartment in Kips Bay. I told Abbey I had to drop off a package that belongs to her Uncle Philip. Angie, Shirley, Chrisy, Billie and Patrick, Max and Jed, plus Bob and Dave were all in attendance. Chrisy and Angie arranged to have 100 red helium-filled balloons delivered for her living room ceiling, to compliment Abbey's

148

red eyeglass frames. I played Dusty Springfield's greatest hits as Abbey opened the door and turned on the lights to whistles and cheers. I arranged for thin crust pizzas from John's, Abbey's favorite. Of course, Abbey started crying.

WEDNESDAY AUGUST 18, 1982

Jim called from San Francisco. He was very upset. Sandy has a drug problem. He was arrested and charged with possession of drugs. Sandy spends his evenings in disco clubs with shady characters. It's a mess. Jim's not sure what to do. Sandy may be stealing money from Jim. He's not sure. I told him to first take care of himself. Sandy may be a chameleon. Get a safe deposit box at Wells Fargo. Maybe it's time to think about living on your own. What a mess. I felt badly for Jim. He's like a flower child. He's so naïve. I told Jim, Abbey and I would stay in touch.

THURSDAY AUGUST 19, 1982

Lots to cover in group therapy tonight. It's my session #11.

This was Graham and Peter's off weekend away from the Pines. They actually missed it; all that sexual excitement. Graham wondered if they should have taken a full share after all. But the $5,000 price tag seemed too steep. Being locked up in Manhattan in the August heat was almost unbearable. Graham declared to the group, "Next year a full share."

Last weekend was a red flag weekend—Graham and Peter were away, so Eric and Aaron went wild. Aaron picked up an olive-skinned nineteen-year-old hustler from Sayville on the Pines ferry. He charged a flat rate of $250 for both of them for the weekend. He was their willing sex slave for two days straight. They never had so much sex in just two days. Of course, they eventually bonded and by the time they boarded the ferry back to Sayville the kid told them his life story over a fish dinner on the mainland. Their treat. The kid's name was Eugenio. Eric made sure he got the kid's number.

149

Darko and Jerry had an argument over renting hustlers for spicy threesomes. Darko doesn't want to pitch in 50% since he just watches Jerry go crazy with these guys. He gave Jerry an ultimatum: no outside sex, period, plus Jerry must move-in with him or they part ways. Jerry was stunned. He left almost immediately. "I have to think about this Darko. You're asking a lot. Give me some time; I'll get back to you." Terrence shook Darko's hand and gave him a hug. "Good for you Darko."

Steve reported he's falling deeply in love with Gordon. He realized it when Gordon confided in him that he's afraid Steve will leave him for a younger man. Steve told Gordon he had had the same fear regarding Gordon. Once they cleared that up, they felt a lot closer.

Brandon has yet to buy any colored bandanas. But he hasn't ruled them out either. He needs time to figure out what he wants. He and Jason had dinner last week. Brandon felt overwhelmed by Jason and all his same old demands, as if Jason had no appreciation for what Brandon was going through after eight years together. Brandon was actually relieved when he got back to his own apartment on Christopher Street away from Jason. He took Larry out for dinner the next night. It made him feel stronger. Terrence asked Brandon what he meant by that. "Jason was suffocating me with all his demands for his selfish nonsense. Larry makes me feel good about myself. Who gives a shit if we fly first class to London? Nothing is real anymore with Jason. He's just caught up in the consumption game. More of this, more of that. I'm tired of all of it. I just want a man who loves me, a man I can love back." Terrence gave Brandon a long hug. "Nice work Brandon. Keep it up."

I told the group about Abbey's birthday weekend in the Pines; the highpoint was making love in the sand dunes. Plus, Abbey's surprise birthday party back in the city at Angie's apartment in Kips Bay.

I concluded with Jim's upsetting phone call over Sandy and drugs. Terrence asked me how did it make me feel? "Sorry for Jim. But also critical of Jim. He should have seen this coming. He threw away our nine-year relationship for a disco twinkie. But Jim is a good person. He deserves more. I just hope he figures it all out. He doesn't believe in therapy like I do. He's isolated. I worry about him." Terrence advised me well. "Keep in touch with Jim. Share Abbey with him. You and Abbey are good role models for Jim."

FRIDAY AUGUST 20, 1982

Douglas invited Abbey and me over for dinner in his loft. Strictly dinner, no sex this time around. He was so cute. The food was takeout from Chinatown. Douglas can't boil water. He just wanted to meet Abbey and congratulate us both on our budding relationship. He told us he's never been able to keep a relationship alive. They always slip away in a few weeks. He misses what we take for granted every day.

He proudly showed us his collection of gay photographers: Bruce Weber, Tom Bianchi, Robert Mapplethorpe and Alvin Baltrop. He has spent time with all of them. They are his friends. Plus, he showed us some of his own pictures. Douglas has natural talent. They were almost all male nudes, really beautiful.

I thanked Douglas for looking after me when Jim and I broke up. He practically saved my life. Douglas hugged me. He said he'd always had his eye on me. I was flattered, especially since I find Douglas so sexy, so butch. He said if Abbey and I ever felt like a threesome, he'd be honored. Nothing heavy. Abbey said that sounded great. He'd really enjoy that. When we parted, Douglas hugged Abbey.

SATURDAY AUGUST 21, 1982

Abbey and I love to walk in the city. It's really the only way to take it all in. We often walk from the loft, through Tribeca and Soho, up Fifth Avenue to Midtown. Occasionally we run into someone famous. That happened today on Madison in the 30s. The sidewalk wasn't crowded. Walking towards us in the opposite direction was Andy Warhol. He was all alone. He was unmistakable with his mop of blond straw hair. As we crossed paths, I smiled and called out, "Hey, Andy! How's it going?" He didn't lose a beat. He just kept walking with his usual deadpan expression. I love that sort of thing.

Inside the central hall in Grand Central Station, we sat down on a travertine bench to take in the sights. People in a rush everywhere. The ceiling 60-feet overhead is a night sky with a thousand twinkling stars. The enormous glass windows which fill the two opposite side walls are amazing. Abbey spotted a guy walking inside the windows thirty-some-feet in the air on a steel and glass catwalk. I grabbed Abbey's hand. "Let's get up there. That would be so cool. I'll find a way." Sure enough, I did. The catwalks had thick glass floors. From up there you felt yourself flying over the enormous room, just like in Peter Pan, with stars overhead.

Sunday August 22, 1982

We had brunch at Cornelia Street Café with Chrisy. She's still getting over my brother Mark. Abbey got her laughing with a few dirty jokes. He's great that way. He's a real people person. Must be the Jewish thing with everybody talking nonstop around the dining table.

Chrisy lives in a garret apartment on Perry Street in the Village. Really tiny, but very romantic. It reminded us of the kind of place Mimi might live in, in La Boheme. Chrisy knew we loved her apartment. Out of the blue, she offered it to us for next weekend. She's visiting her parents in Connecticut. What a treat.

Monday August 23, 1982

Abbey and I are big fans of the painter Mark Rothko. Abbey suggested I try my hand at painting a look alike. I have a big art book on Rothko, full of wonderful pictures of his paintings. We settled on our favorite and I picked up the largest stretched canvas I could find on Canal Street, plus more oil paint. I tried a staining technique using rags to smear the paint around. No brushes. It had soft edges like a real Rothko. It was mostly red, orange, pink and olive. The undercoat was red. I carefully measured Rothko's proportions for the colored rectangles. It looked pretty amazing in the end. Most people will think it's the real thing worth millions.

TUESDAY AUGUST 24, 1982

My Canadian friend Chuck is throwing a big party at his lover's townhouse on Gansevoort Street. Chuck just got his official American citizenship. Chuck and John were both busy taking care of their two circles of friends. John's friends are all writers, Chuck's are all ex-tricks he's picked up over the years. The two circles are largely separate from each other. It's a strange arrangement, but it seems to suit them well. I couldn't imagine Abbey and me living like that.

WEDNESDAY AUGUST 25, 1982

I called Jim tonight. He moved out of the apartment he was living in with Sandy. He's staying temporarily with a new friend from the pottery studio he belongs to. Jim sounded surprisingly calm, like it was all for the best. He said things would sort themselves out in time. He loves the Castro. He also opened a new banking account in his name only. He's concerned Sandy may be stealing money from him.

THURSDAY AUGUST 26, 1982

Tonight will be my 12th group therapy session. It should be interesting.

Graham had his first run-in with their Pines housemate named Theo. When he and Peter arrived early Friday afternoon, Theo was in their bed with a super-cute hustler he'd picked up on the ferry. Otherwise the house was empty. Embarrassed, Theo invited Graham and Peter to join him in a foursome. Theo picked up the tab. It was the perfect way to kick-off the weekend. Apparently Theo's mattress is a twin, while Graham's is a king.

Eric and Aaron played it cool in the Pines. Aaron grilled fish. A little dancing at the Pavilion. They had a long walk Sunday morning to Water Island. Eric said the highpoint of the weekend was definitely the secluded sex in the dunes.

Darko hasn't heard back from Jerry. He's worried. Terrence suggested Darko set up a meeting with Jerry in a neutral space like the Central Park Zoo. He said the animals are always a good distraction from our problems. "If it goes well, maybe have dinner in a quiet restaurant nearby. Just relax, stay cool. Remember you may be talking to your future husband."

Steve wants Gordon to meet his older sister, Janice, a chemist, and his brother-in-law Richard, an anthropologist. They both teach at Columbia. Steve is close to his only sister. He has already told her all about Gordon. She wants to cook dinner for them soon. Sounds terrific. Gordon is all excited.

Meanwhile, they had the Neptune house all to themselves last weekend. They got stoned, put on Procol Harum's hit A Salty Dog. Perfect background music for some extended action in the sling.

Brandon was so cute tonight. He broke down and bought his first pair of 501s, a vintage leather motorcycle jacket and two bandanas, light blue and dark blue. He actually wore them all to group. What a transformation. He really looked the part. He keeps the dark blue bandana in his rear left pocket and the pale blue bandana in his rear right pocket. He said it's all a bit confusing; basically, he likes to get fucked and give head. He's your basic queer, like me. He's spent a few evenings in Julius' and the Ramrod. It's been thrilling, especially the Ramrod, mostly just watching, talking to the bartenders and a few friendly guys. One guy in the Ramrod gave his ass a friendly squeeze. Brandon got his number. Brandon's in no hurry; he's just taking it all in. Terrence congratulated Brandon and gave him a super long hug. He reminded Brandon to always play safe. The group gave him a standing ovation with plenty of hoots. Brandon shed a tear.

I told them all about Douglas's dinner for Abbey and me in his loft and his offer to host a threesome if we're ever interested, which, of course, we both are. I also told the group that Jim moved out of the Castro apartment he was sharing with Sandy. Terrence asked me how did that make me feel? "Relieved for Jim. I don't want to see Jim get hurt." "So, you are less critical of Jim now?" "Yes, absolutely. I will always love Jim."

Friday August 27, 1982

Tonight was a Friday Shabbat dinner at Shirley's. Abbey wanted to invite Angie as well. Great idea. Shirley loved Angie the moment she met her. They are both strong independent Jewish women. Shirley is planning a fall tour to Paris with her girlfriend Hilda. It will be another educational Tauck Tour. Abbey loves Hilda. She's like family, a German Jew who fled the Nazis. Shirley made her potato latkes.

Sunday August 29, 1982

Early Saturday morning Abbey and I headed out to the Pines. It was our weekend visit as guests of Jack and Wolf. They rented a gorgeous Horace Gifford house on Bay Walk near the east end. Horace was the top Pines architect in the 60s. He designed over sixty modernist houses in the Pines. I love them all. Poor Horace was arrested with his pants down, his cock up some guy's ass, in a midnight raid of the Meat Rack. His name was in the newspaper. It ruined his career.

Jack and Wolf were just wonderful. They spoiled us silly. Wonderful meals, nice long intimate conversations, quiet beach walks and of course plenty of communal sex in their large hot tub. Wolf's cock was the centerpiece. Perfect proportions. Really gorgeous. Wolf is completely relaxed about sharing God's gift. He knows white guys always want to give him head. Abbey and I really worked it, driving Wolf crazy. Jack was totally cool with anything oral. Wolf and Jack are both totally bonkers in love. It's beautiful to witness.

Monday August 30, 1982

I signed up for the intermediate oil painting class at New York University. It's being taught by Daniel again. I really enjoyed his first class. He's a great instructor. Brings out the best in everyone. First class is in two weeks on a Tuesday.

Tuesday August 31, 1982

Jed's Max called me up at SOM this morning. He's terrific. His melanoma cancer is under control. He wants to celebrate. He's invited Jed, Abbey and me to join him at Windows on the World atop the World Trade Center. His treat. I told him absolutely. First, let's toast Max and Jed with a glass of champaign at my loft. It's only two short blocks away from WTC.

What a view! The glass goes right down to the floor. It made Abbey a little queasy. I loved it. The city lights were spectacular. Since we were all dressed in leather, they gave us the royal treatment with a cute hot German waiter named Hans. Hans took extra special care of us. What a basket on this kid. TDF. How about Hans for dessert?

Wednesday September 1, 1982

I'm so happy, I can't stop smiling. Abbey surprised me. It's Wednesday night and I was about ready to call Abbey at his mother's apartment for our usual mid-week nightly chat. I heard the door unlock at the other end of the loft. Abbey appeared with a mischievous grin on his face. He was holding something behind his back. Then he turned around. He was holding a pillow. He was holding his favorite pillow. It goes back to his childhood. He takes it with him wherever he sleeps. This was his way of telling me he's officially moving in. Tonight marks our three-month anniversary. I'm ecstatic! My beloved has arrived.

Thursday September 2, 1982

I called up Wolf to thank him for our weekend in the Pines. I wished him well at New York University. Classes start today. This will be Wolf's final year. He's an economics major. He still has to figure out what he wants to do after graduation. It varies greatly, from a Wall Street analyst in a three-piece suit to the owner of Chelsea's hottest new gym/cafe. Jack has already declared he will support Wolf 100% in whatever he wants to do. That's really cool.

Tonight is my group therapy session with Terrence and my buddies. It's session #13.

Graham always goes first. Terrence likes to keep our speaking order the same each week. He told us once it helps people relax. I think he's right about that. Terrence is terrific.

This was an off Pines weekend for Graham and Peter. Feeling trapped in their airconditioned apartment, Peter got to thinking and proposed to Graham that they call up a gay escort service and order takeout, a cute call boy. They'd never done such a thing before. It sounded crazy, but after all they have seen on Fire Island, why not? So, Peter called in and asked for a Tex, "a stud, like the cowboy present in Boys in the Band." Terrence asked how it went? Graham chuckled, "What do you think darling!"

Eric and Aaron had the place to themselves, thank God. After a two-week break they were both seriously horny. They went "shopping" Saturday morning in the Rack, and came back to the cottage with a teenage Hispanic guy who liked to screw. Apparently, the three of them were making quite a ruckus. Someone from the main house came over to complain, but ended up getting screwed himself. The Pines can get a little crazy. Good thing Graham and Peter weren't around. Graham jumped in, interrupting Eric, "Sorry, we picked the wrong weekend to be away." The whole group had a good laugh.

Darko took Terrence seriously and set up a date with Jerry in the Penguin House at the Central Park Zoo. It's pretty secluded. Jerry started kissing Darko passionately. It got out of hand pretty quickly. Darko gave Jerry a sensational blowjob. Jerry did the same for Darko. As happy as two clams, they had lunch at the Copper Kettle nearby on Madison. Jerry announced he wants to move in with Darko. No more tearooms. He's getting too old. But he thinks they will need a two-bedroom apartment given all the shit they both have. Darko agreed. Jerry has a realtor friend.

Sunday Steve and Gordon had dinner at Steve's sister Janice. Her husband Richard, the anthropologist, brought up the topic of gay sex. Apparently, he will soon be publishing a serious academic article on the subject in some high-brow anthropology journal. He wanted to know all about our sexual practices and how they compared with his academic theories. It all sounded a bit bizarre, but Steve was eager to share their favorite kinky sex routines. He used the recent example from last weekend, in the S&M house on Neptune. Steve and Gordon were all alone, lights dimmed, lots of candles, naked except for their leather harnesses and jock straps, a little stoned, with the stereo turned up loud. Condoms in place they went at it taking turns fucking in time to the music. That's how gay men make love. "So, what do you think Richard?" Richard was speechless.

Brandon called up the guy who squeezed his ass in the Ramrod. His name is Stanley. Stanley was very direct on the phone. "So, I see by your bandanas you like to get fucked and give head, right?" "Well yes, that along with a few other things, like cooking a great dinner. Might I interest you in the latter for starters?" Brandon had us laughing in tears. Their dinner date was a huge success. Stanley arrived with a bouquet of roses and apologized for his forward phone manner. Brandon's gay response, "Don't apologize darling, I like my men rough!" After a superb dinner at One Christopher Street, Brandon finally got from Stanley what he had advertised for down on the street, a proper butt-fucking and the cock-suck of his dreams.

I told the group about Abbey's pillow and what that means for our relationship. Terrence asked me to explain. "It means Abbey and Miles are now completely committed to each other, just like a straight married couple. Abbey is the new center of my life. He is my beloved. All our future journeys through life will be shared together. I will never be alone again." Terrence hugged me. I cried. The group gave me the best group hug ever.

FRIDAY SEPTEMBER 3, 1982

What a bombshell! A major melt down at SOM. One third of the entire staff has been laid off, including me, effective immediately. Bob was spared. They lost their major client, the Saudi Royal Family. It's all tied to the global supply of oil. Everyone is in a state of shock. The office feels like a morgue.

I called up my English friend John. We worked together at SOM several years ago. He knew Jim well. When John's first marriage fell apart, we became closer. When Jim left, John stood by my side. So, we were an odd pair of widows, one straight, the other gay. I love John. He has a dry British sense of humor that always makes me smile. When John left SOM he joined a small Canadian healthcare firm that has a tiny satellite office in New York City. I knew John liked working there. He thought I'd fit right in. John suggested I drop by and chat with the senior partner Michael. I have an interview set up for after Labor Day, September 7th.

SUNDAY SEPTEMBER 4-5, 1982

This is the weekend Chrisy has given Abbey and me the keys to her tiny garret apartment on Perry Street. It's a welcome distraction after the SOM shock. The apartment is on the top third floor of a modest red brick townhouse. Very romantic. It's smack dab in the middle of Gayville. Feels like the baths in broad daylight. Cute guys everywhere you look. A nonstop parade of hot bubble butts. It's almost too much. Really a gay ghetto. Quite a switch from the deserted streets on weekends around us in the Bennett Building. Down there we hardly see a soul on weekends.

Abbey wants to have dinner out at Café de la Gare, his favorite. Afterwards, I beg him for a pitstop at the backroom of the Stud. I need a serious distraction. He's as interested as I am. It's a Friday night, so it's packed, wall-to-wall cocksuckers. You can smell the poppers, hear guys slurping as they suck harder, other guys moaning softly, bare asses being slapped. Some butch guy grabs us in the dark, rips open our Levi's and jerks us off together with one hand for each. He's a pro. It's just what we both needed tonight. Raunchy queer sex at the Stud. It's been ages.

Sunday morning we have brunch at Black Sheep near the Hudson and then wander up to the abandoned Pier 52 for a little gay sunbathing on the rear deck overlooking the Hudson. Guys are wandering inside for kinky sex. We're not interested. The water is a steely gray. It's almost too chilly for nude sunbathing. Labor Day is tomorrow already. Summer is almost over.

MONDAY SEPTEMBER 6, 1982

It's Labor Day. It's a tradition. Squeezing into the overcrowded bus to Jones Beach. What a contrast to the Pines. Jim and I used to do it before we discovered bliss on Fire Island. Jones Beach was so urban, so intense, so extremely ethnic, mostly brown skins, heavy cruising in the public showers with guys getting gladly butt- fucked in the stalls. Outside on the beach, towels spread out touching, packed together like sardines, with blaring boom boxes, the stench of coconut oil, the busy hot dog stand and sand all over everything, especially inside your pockets. To the east nude gay sunbathers and tucked in the sand dunes gay butt-fuckers. By 4:00 pm we'd be exhausted, worn out by the sun and noise, ready for the crowded bus back to the Big Apple.

TUESDAY SEPTEMBER 7, 1982

It was hardly a job interview, more like a party or a celebration. The senior partner Michael was a slick salesman. He knew just how to flatter while still sounding sincere. Mr. Charm. Full of dirty jokes and shocking stories. I really liked the guy.

He clearly wanted me bad. He had done his homework. He knew my

160

pedigree, my track record, my connections to the intellectual elite in my profession. I was the type of person he needed standing next to him, to place himself on a pedestal, to get him inside the big tent, to make him a "player."

He didn't even crack open my portfolio. Not necessary. "When can you start?" I figured, if John spoke so well of the guy, who am I to question? I said, "Right away."

WEDNESDAY SEPTEMBER 8, 1982

Compared to SOM, the Canadian's satellite office was a shoebox. Well actually, a pair of shoeboxes. A front room office/conference room. And a backroom studio with three workstations. On Central Park West, in the upper 60s, ground floor walk-in, like a doctor's suite. It didn't go unnoticed by me, that the office was across the street from the infamous Ramble.

I sat in the backroom with the Brit John and Sour Virginia. Michael favored me from the get-go. I was to be his lead designer. John was technical support; Virginia was a foil Michael used to ramp up my work to the next level. He knew I was gay, no problem, creative people are always different, a little queer. He knew I loved the ballet and opera. Perfect, that fit nicely into his polished self-image. It was an enormous shift from SOM. I still wore a suit and tie, but it really wasn't necessary. I wasn't in the big leagues any more.

THURSDAY SEPTEMBER 9, 1982

Tonight is session # 14 for my group therapy with Terrence.

This was a Pines weekend for Graham and Peter. Their favorite housemate Trevor, the geriatric psychiatrist, was also out. Trevor proposed a morning walk to Cherry Grove, before it got too warm. Trevor took a few detours through the Rack, showing off the sights.

Eric and Aaron laid low. They worked out together at the Botel Gym for several hours. All pumped up, the sex back at the cottage was particularly hot. Walked to Cherry Grove for dinner at Top of the Bay. Water taxi back. Another round of sex in bed.

Darko and Jerry must have looked at more than a dozen two-bedroom apartments with their realtor, a short Jewish princess named Sylvia, with over-the-top eye make-up and a loud whining voice. Most were awful with light-well views, tiny bathrooms, roach-infested kitchens. You can imagine. But what a miracle, the last one on the tour was a hidden jewel in Brooklyn Heights on Henry Street, a four-story walkup. Sun lit rooms, high ceilings, moldings, parquet wood floors, even a real working fireplace. Darko and Jerry signed the lease on the spot. They are ecstatic!

Steve reported his sister Janice was still laughing over the gay sex incident. Richard told her he is rethinking the whole article from scratch and may want to speak with Steve and Gordon at some point about some details. Steve said sure, any time. He suggested Richard might want to do a weekend in the Pines interviewing guys. He could always spend a night in the Botel or use the guest bedroom at Neptune. He could even tour the Rack in moonlight.

Brandon and Stanley are getting along famously. It turns out Stanley can be extremely charming when he wants to be. It certainly helps that the sex between them is red hot. They also both share a deep appreciation for the opera. They have bought tickets to opening night at the Met on Tuesday September 21st. They will be seeing Strauss' Der Rosenkavalier starring Kiri Te Kanawa. In the meantime, Brandon is busy in the kitchen.

Terrence asked me how I felt about leaving SOM and starting the new job. I told him it was fine. I like to try out different job experiences, compare them. Small, medium and large firms; they all have their pluses and minuses. In a small firm I have a greater impact, but I enjoy the complexity of large projects that always end up in the really large firms. It's a trade-off. This new smaller firm is fine for now. I'll see where it leads.

Friday September 10, 1982

Tonight was our long-awaited threesome with Douglas, Abbey and me. We met up after work in Douglas's loft in the Bennett Building. This will be a first-time encounter for Abbey with Douglas; Douglas and I have fooled around a few times in the past. Sex for Douglas is completely egoless, he really gets into it, but it's never heavy. He's always gentle. He's a butt-fuck pro using his vintage sling in creative ways. Abbey and I discussed it all beforehand and agreed the best approach in a threesome, is to let everyone sample everything equally. No master and slave crap. That way egos disappear and we all have fun together. We all had a great time. Douglas was so loving. We really bonded. I love both Abbey and Douglas like my brothers. Afterwards, we went out for lite Szechuan in Chinatown.

Saturday September 11, 1982

I had an unexplained urge to roller-skate on the huge open plaza of the World Trade Center early this morning. I asked Abbey to join me. It was a perfect cloudless cobalt sky. Afterwards, lying on our backs looking straight up, the twin silver towers were magnificent in the brilliant sunlight, like a pair of gigantic crystalline glaciers afloat in a blue sea. I noticed a tiny jet much further away, a minuscule white wedge, so insignificant against the cobalt sky. Perhaps the morning flight from JFK to Rome. I missed Venice and its smelly lagoon. I thought back fondly on my brief encounter with my Venetian gondolier. I hoped he was well. I glanced at my watch for some reason. I noticed it was 9:03 am.

Sunday September 12, 1982

It was a lazy afternoon. Abbey and I were bored. He proposed a walk-through tour of the Hellfire Club. I liked the idea. I felt safe with Abbey at my side. It's in the basement of an abandoned triangular red brick building close to the Hudson. Maybe five-stories. Nothing special. An unmarked door. The smell of stale poppers. The entrance to hell. We wore our leather jackets, our armor. The bouncer smiled at Abbey. Inside, we watched a New York City cop give a Hispanic kid a blowjob, or so it looked. It was the real uniform alright, just not on a real cop. The guy getting fucked in the sling sure looked familiar as he moaned in pleasure, maybe our bank vice president, who knows. His master, the Devil, was shirtless in tight black leather chaps and a leather head mask. The trim guy waiting in line next for the sling could be anyone. It's Sunday, everybody has the day off. Go get fucked. Why not, even in hell. We just watched. No touching. Back outside the sun was blinding. The fresh air felt good.

Monday September 13, 1982

My new office has a British receptionist named Anne. I love her. She has the cutest English accent, the real thing. It goes perfectly with her sweet motherly manner. I scraped my finger slightly while setting up my new workstation. Out came the witch hazel, the alcohol, the Neosporin, the Band-Aids. Anne played nurse. She took my temperature. Really, for a finger scrape? And, how about some fresh English tea to smooth things over?

Michael hired her for her golden silky voice, that endearing accent that every client would fall in love with. They'd call just to hear her pick up the phone; to have her ask them how they were feeling, how their day was going thus far. As if it might swing upward at any moment.

Tuesday September 14, 1982

I started my intermediate oil painting class tonight at New York University. Daniel is the instructor again. Only eight students total. Four were with me in the intro class. It runs for eight weeks. One of the new faces definitely looks gay. A shy Hispanic kid named Jose. A puppy dog. Moist brown eyes. He's super quiet. Daniel asked him to sit near him so he can hear him more easily.

Daniel jumps right in with a few painting exercises to get us warmed up. First, painting a concave surface, then painting a convex surface. Next, painting a still life with only warm colors, then painting the same still life using only cold colors. Last, he asks each of us to pair up and quickly paint a portrait of one another, as realistic or fantastic as we wish. Of course, I paired up with Jose. I did the first four exercises at lightning speed so that I could really focus on the portrait of Jose for the remaining hour and a half. I really wanted to make him look gorgeous. Actually, he is gorgeous, I just made him look supernatural. I painted him nude sitting on a massive tilted stone block, his whole body leaning forward slightly, his head cradled in one hand, with the elbow resting on a raised knee. The opposite leg and arm are extended straight down to the ground. Strong opaque shadows and rich fleshy pinks, yellows and burgundies for the skin. The background is definitely entirely black except for a deep orange partial wall behind the central figure. Brilliant clear light sweeps across his slightly downturned face. He looks like an athlete. It's a homage to Caravaggio.

Daniel has been paying close attention. When the class is over, he pulls me aside. "Miles, your painting has really taken a quantum leap forward. I want to place you in my advanced oil painting class. You are showing real promise. It's a smaller class, just three students, plus you. It meets the same days, but from 10:00-12:00. How does that sound?" "Fantastic."

WEDNESDAY SEPTEMBER 15, 1982

I took the day off to paint at home. I'm having a ball. No time for my diary.

THURSDAY SEPTEMBER 16, 1982

Tonight was group therapy session #15. Terrence looked stressed out.

This was an off Pines weekend for Graham and Peter. Peter picked up a few guide books to Rome in Barnes & Noble. He's been thinking about a trip to Rome in the fall with Graham, maybe ten days in mid-October when the weather is the best. Graham's birthday is October 19th. It would be their first big trip together.

Eric and Aaron had the cottage to themselves. They invited Larry out for the weekend. He's a cute gay co-worker from their office. Aaron has always had the hots for Larry. Since the tiny cottage has only one bedroom, Aaron suggested Larry join he and Eric in the king-size bed. Eric reported they sandwiched Larry between them and serviced him all night long taking turns. Larry loved it. He's a real slut. He even asked if he could maybe come back again before the season was over. Aaron said sure, why not?

Darko and Jerry worked on their new Brooklyn Heights apartment all weekend. They sanded the wood floor, did some light touch-up painting, installed new locks, shopped for a new firm mattress. They enjoyed Middle Eastern food on nearby Atlantic Avenue, delicious and cheap. They walked the Promenade and discovered just how cruisy it is. A guy asked them if they'd like a threesome back at his apartment. Jerry replied, "Can't you see? We're newlyweds."

For some unknown reason Steve and Gordon were sexually on fire all weekend. They stayed holed up in the dark beach shack on Neptune the entire weekend. They even wore their leather harnesses 24/7. Their neighbor dropped in when he overheard all the moaning and butt slapping. The house is definitely a sex den.

Brandon called Jason and told him he was seriously involved with Stanley and had no plans to return to their previous arrangement. Jason took it calmly. It seemed like he hardly gave a shit. Meanwhile, Brandon and Stanley have a fun new game. They bought two complete sets of those colored sex bandanas from the Christopher Street Bookshop, one set for each of them. First, they each dress independently for cruising Christopher Street. Pick out the bandana that suits their wildest desires at the moment, carefully place it in the correct pocket and then hit Christopher Street. If you score, signal the other for a threesome upstairs in the apartment. Or just pick up each other and follow the instructions on the colored bandana.

I had nothing to report. I thanked my buddies for being so cool.

Friday September 17, 1982

Tonight is Rosh Hashana, the Jewish New Year. Abbey and I are invited to his cousin Judy's loft on Cornelia Street for a big family dinner. Some twenty-five people. My first introduction to Abbey's extended family. I'm excited. This kind of event never happens in my family. It's noisy. Everybody is animated. It's all very Jewish. Super cool. I love Judy. Abbey told me all about her months ago. Now I get to finally meet her. First thing I spotted on the way in, was a pair of Andy Warhol soup can lithographs in the living room. Wow! Judy made me feel like family. Afterwards, I told Abbey we're definitely having Judy down to the loft for dinner sometime in the next month.

Saturday September 18, 1982

This weekend is my first of two back-to-back EST Trainings. Sixty hours over four days. Intense. Abbey talked me into it. He did it with Joel a year ago and said it really impowered him to break through some personal barriers. Communication skills. I could use some help in that department. I'm a bit skeptical. It comes out of Werner Erhard from San Francisco. They're all a little nuts; I mentioned it to Jim and Philip. They thought it was "way cool." Hardly any free time to write in my diary.

Monday September 20, 1982

After work I met with my well-to-do friend Robert from the Saint to review my schematic design for his new house in P-town. A few weeks ago, he had sent me site drawings, dozens of site photos and his space program of what should be included in the project. Robert is as anal as I am which makes the process easy. He's an ideal client. He knows how to articulate clearly what he wants. Too bad that doesn't apply to his sex performance in bed. Otherwise, we'd have made a great couple. Anyway, he loves the design; he doesn't want to change a thing. It's a clean simple modern design, lots of glass, passive solar, poured in place concrete, butterfly roof with large eaves to shade the windows. It's sited back from the ocean to protect the main dune and give the house total privacy. I told Robert he could be a nudist and still be completely comfortable. Zero chance of that. He wants me to proceed to the next phase, design development and work up preliminary cost numbers.

4

FALL

TUESDAY SEPTEMBER 21, 1982

It's the first day of fall.

Tonight was opening night for the 1982-83 season of the Metropolitan Opera in Lincoln Center. Abbey and I splurged and bought tickets in the Dress Circle, a small fortune. They are doing Strauss' Der Rosenkavlier starring Kiri Te Kanawa. Abbey and I dressed "high culture butch," black boots, new black 501's, black pressed Calvin Klein tees under black leather vests. We saw plenty of opera queens in their black leather during the intermissions, including Jack and Wolf, of course, and Brandon and Stanley from my therapy group. The opera was outstanding. The only complaint was Pavarotti canceled at the last moment, out sick; his replacement could barely hit his notes.

I introduced Abbey to Brandon and Stanley. Abbey actually knows Stanley from their GAA days years ago. Brandon announced that he and Stanley are flying to London in the morning for a one-week "honeymoon." Staying at the Savoy. Brandon sort of inherited the hotel reservation and a pair of first-class airplane tickets from his ex, Jason, who didn't want them anymore. Brandon figured, it's his loss and their gain.

Afterwards, on the way home, I told Abbey I want to take him to London for Christmas. It would be his first trip to Europe. He went nuts. He thinks London at Christmas sounds very romantic. He's so adorable. He thinks we should read aloud Charles Dicken's A Christmas Carol before we leave to get in the mood.

Wednesday September 22, 1982

Over lunch I popped into British Airways to buy a pair of tickets for London. Also got the latest guide book. This will be my first European trip since Jim left me. I'm expecting traveling with Abbey will be more fun than my trips with uptight Jim. Abbey is already psyched. He's checking out the Indian restaurants. London is world-famous for the best Indian food on the planet.

Thursday September 23, 1982

Tonight is group therapy session #16.

Graham and Peter have picked dates for their fall trip to Rome, October 10th to the 16th. Graham will miss a therapy session. Out in the Pines it was their turn to prepare Saturday night's dinner for twelve. Graham is a serious cook. Peter played his assistant. They were in the kitchen all afternoon preparing an elaborate Indian feast. Finally, when the dinner bell sounded at 10 o'clock, Graham appeared in a silk sari and a gold turban. Dinner lasted over two hours. Afterwards, the whole house headed over to the Pavilion to dance off some calories.

Graham and Peter stretched the house rules a bit and invited Eric and Aaron from the cottage over for their dinner in the main house. Graham figured that after all that hard work, he was entitled.

Eric and Aaron were on their best behavior since they were now dinner guests. Of course, they were also invited to swim in the pool. It was just an excuse to get a good look at them in their skimpy Speedos. They both have chunky wrestler bods.

Darko reported that he and Jerry are now officially living in the new apartment in Brooklyn Heights. They are two love birds. They've started jogging on the Promenade together, four laps each so far. Jerry thinks their sex has gotten better as a result.

Steve and Gordon were still hot on Neptune. Gordon invited an ex-boyfriend for the weekend named Clint. Gordon knew beforehand that Clint was not into sling sex, so they retired it for the weekend. It was a welcome change. So they went strictly oral. Clint is extra well-hung so no one complained. Afterwards, Steve told Gordon he's getting tired of sling sex. He misses those wonderful blowjobs from Gordon. Gordon was touched and gave Steve an extra-long blowjob on the spot. Now they're both on fire for oral cock. The group erupted in hoots and hollers! Terrence hugged Steve, "Thanks for sharing that Steve. I think we can all relate. Queer cock, up close and personal, is beautiful."

I mostly talked about Rosh Hashana at Judy's, about how easily Abbey's extended family reached out to me. They made me feel welcome. That means a lot.

Terrence announced that Brandon and Stanley were in London this week. He brought a white layer cake to celebrate all the couples in the group— Graham and Peter/ Eric and Aaron/ Darko and Jerry/ Steve and Gordon/ Abbey and Miles and out on their honeymoon Brandon and Stanley. Terrence was beaming. "This marks a first in my group therapy practice. I'm so proud of all of you. Six beautiful loving couples. Congratulations everyone!"

Friday September 24, 1982

After dinner at the Vietnamese restaurant in Sheridan Square, Abbey and I headed west on Christopher to the Barn for disco dancing with the Hispanic kids. They are always thrilled to see Abbey. He knows them well. He loves this young crowd so cheerful and full of energy. All sweaty and shirtless; they can dance nonstop for hours. I mostly just watched and chatted with the famous DJ Manuel, a hip Hispanic guy.

I spotted Mr. Jock Strap at the bar. Remember the Hispanic guy from the Wall Street Sauna last winter? He was my introduction to raunchy queer sex. We hooked up a few times. "Can I buy you a drink? I'm Miles. This is my boyfriend Abbey. I know you from the Wall Street Sauna last winter. You were into jock straps just like me."

"I think I remember you. You were on fire. You asked me to fuck you. I'm Mateo. Maybe we could get together sometime. Why don't you both come as my guests next Wednesday to New York Jocks, the Soho jerkoff club. I'm a member. The guys are really hot. You'll have a good time. Think you can handle it?"

"You bet; we'll see you there Mateo. Wear your jock strap." "Great Miles. Next Wednesday, 98 Wooster, 7 o'clock."

Sunday September 26, 1982

My last weekend at the EST Training. Locked away for two days for over thirty hours. Pretty intense. By the time it was over, my head was numb. Was it worth all that money? I'd have to say hopefully yes.

Monday September 27, 1982

At work Michael was all excited. An office project for a neighborhood health clinic in Brooklyn that I designed was selected for a New York City

AIA design award. Michael congratulated me. He always craves public recognition, so this was a big deal. I set up a photo shoot on Wednesday. Michael was busy talking it up with his favorite senior editor from Architectural Record over a 2-hour martini lunch. That's Michael.

TUESDAY SEPTEMBER 28, 1982

Tonight was my first advanced oil painting class. It was very intimate, just four students total including me, plus Daniel. Split evenly between two gals, Sonia and Peggy, and two guys, Angelo and me. Of course, I was partial to Angelo right off the bat. I mean, he was gorgeous. How was I supposed to paint sitting next to this hunk? Plus, he was old school, his beautifully shaded figure sketches looked like something Leonardo might have knocked out. When I introduced myself, he smiled warmly as all Italians do. "Ciao, I'm Angelo, I'm from Firenze, home of Michelangelo. I'm here as an exchange student with the University of Florence."

Daniel had us paint from life a pair of nude figures, male and female. It was very challenging. My figures looked stiff, Angelo's were soft and delicate, full of life and expression. Daniel saw I was struggling. He gave me a fresh canvas and told me to start over with feeling. "Make love to your subject. Don't be so timid. Passione! Stop thinking, just paint." It worked, I connected with the models, the man's hunched over muscular frame like a tightened spring, confronting the woman's tall aristocratic head with its regal neck, its long graceful lines.

WEDNESDAY SEPTEMBER 29, 1982

The morning photoshoot in Brooklyn went smoothly. I used a young new gay photographer, Robert, whom I'd met recently in the Pines. He was great. He even included some of the kids from the neighborhood. Michael was pleased.

Tonight's our date with Mateo at New York Jocks in Soho. Mateo showed up as promised. Inside, an enormous open artist's loft. Huge sheets of plastic to protect the furniture and floor. Some twenty horny guys, most buck naked, proudly stroking their cocks while carrying tiny paper cups of Crisco lube. Strutting around like peacocks. Mateo wore his olive-colored jock strap just for me. I pulled it off. His brown butt with white tan lines was super-hot. We paired-up while Abbey slapped our butts. Loud pops. A dozen guys formed a giant circle jerk with us in the middle. More loud pops. Beads of sweat and pools of white cum. A dam burst open. It was wild.

THURSDAY SEPTEMBER 30, 1982

Tonight is group therapy with Terrence. #17.

Graham reported that Peter dropped a bit of a bombshell over the weekend. He got a phone call from Glenda, Peter's ex-girlfriend. Unbeknownst to Graham, Peter had a two-month affair with Glenda, which Peter broke off, when he met Graham. Glenda became- pregnant with Peter's child. She had an abortion which Peter paid for. She's still stuck on Peter and asked to see him. Peter refused and offered her $5,000 to disappear and not return. When Peter finally came clean with Graham, Graham's response was complete surprise, annoyance at being deceived, and sympathy for Glenda. Peter felt terrible. Graham had no idea Peter was bisexual. It really didn't bother him. He just wanted Peter to be honest. He could handle anything; he's still deeply in love with Peter. He just wants everyone to be happy. Graham told Peter he must invite everyone to Peter's apartment so they could meet and talk freely. Peter agreed. Glenda arrived calm. She sat across from Graham and Peter around his dining table talking for hours. Apparently, just the sight of the two men sitting together holding hands touched Glenda deeply. For the first time she understood and accepted Peter's total devotion to Graham. She was able to come around and wished them happiness as a couple. The whole experience left Graham and Peter a bit shaken, but aware for the first time, just how special their relationship was. Terrence congratulated Graham on handling a difficult situation so well.

Eric and Aaron apparently passed the test and were told they were welcome

174

to swim in the pool of the main house any time they wanted, day or night, preferably in the nude. In fact, two guys from the main house joined them for nude swimming on Saturday night and they all ended up humping in the cottage. The cottage has been renamed the "Sex Shack."

Darko reported that on Saturday evening Jerry brought back a trick from the Promenade. $80. Darko was surprised. He thought Jerry's hustler days were behind them. When Jerry realized he had offended Darko, he sent the kid away with a $80 tip for nothing. The rest of the weekend Jerry was all over Darko trying to patch things up. Darko milked the situation. Jerry served him breakfast in bed.

Steve shared how he and Gordon are starting to explore group sex to spice up their oral sex routine. They hang out in the Pines Harbor. Gordon wears his leather pants with a snap-on cod piece. Guys always offer to give him some head. It works every time. Back at the house they have a blowjob fest.

Brandon was just back from the trip to London with Stanley. He was flying like a kite. The Savoy was over-the-top. He's already thinking about the next trip. Maybe something more local. Perhaps Santa Fe, while the opera is on. They could dress up as a couple of cowboy lovers. Maybe stay at one of those gay dude ranches.

I mostly talked about the EST Training and how it compared to our group therapy. I told them I vastly preferred our group. I love you guys and I always look forward to our work together here. EST was impersonal, too rigid, and a little too straight. It was hard for me to open up there. Not like here, where we share absolutely everything. Thanks guys, especially Steve. Terrence gave me a hug.

Last I told them about Abbey and my trip to New York Jocks with Mateo last night. I was so impressed with Mateo. When I first met Mateo last winter at the Wall Street Sauna, I dismissed him as a dumb twinkie. But this time around he was wiser, a master in complete control. We had a good time. Mateo was magnificent. A new friend.

"Nice work guys."

Friday October 1, 1982

Michael could be a little nasty in the office. He'd set up these situations where Virginia and I would compete on the design concept for some new project, as if we were in some big-deal international design competition. In the end, he'd always select me as the winner. It didn't endear Virginia to me. She started to really dislike me. Sure, before I showed up, she was the top dog in the office. Not any longer. I wondered how long she would put up with the situation. She was starting to get openly hostile towards me. With her sour face, she started to remind me of the Wicked Witch of the West.

Sunday October 2-3, 1982

Abbey and I had a 2-day road trip with Chrisy up to Exeter, New Hampshire, primarily to see Louie Kahn's library at the Exeter Academy. All red brick with brick arches everywhere. It's wonderful. Reminds me of ancient Rome. It's a very preppy place, all the cute boys in their navy blazers, gray slacks and sweaters, like a Cadinot flick. Jim went to prepschool here before heading off to Princeton.

We had an argument with Chrisy on the drive back. She was doing all the driving in her car. I really wanted to see the Hartford Seminary in Hartford, Connecticut designed by Richard Meier; one of his white metal panel buildings that I have admired for years. It was an hour out of our way and Chrisy wasn't interested in a long detour. I was furious. It was just a reminder; you probably should never travel with someone you don't already know extremely well.

176

Monday October 4, 1982

Abbey and I had dinner at Café de la Gare with Jimmy, Abbey's best friend from childhood. They grew up together in Great Neck, Long Island and together with a third buddy got into a lot of trouble with things like firecrackers, fireworks, mild explosives, even dangerous chemicals. Your typical bad ass teenagers having fun. Jimmy has since mellowed out, so has Abbey. Jimmy works in the seafood import business and is always getting unbelievable fish for Abbey, free of course. Jimmy's straight and obviously adores Abbey. Nice guy. He told Abbey I made the grade with flying colors, apparently I scored much better than Joel.

Tuesday October 5, 1982

What a fun painting class! Daniel asked us to paint using our favorite color. It could be abstract or representational. He showed us paintings by Robert and Sonia Delaunay for inspiration. I painted a fantastic pair of cobalt and ultramarine blue stallions, running across a darkened gray sky with pink and orange clouds. The horses were magnificent. Free and wild. I'd never painted anything like them before, so virile and strong. Subliminally, I think I was actually painting a double portrait of Abbey and me. The horses were somehow us reincarnated, full of passion and desire.

Wednesday October 6, 1982

I'd been thinking about it for over a week—the Ramble that is. It's literally just across the street from the office. Central Park's major gay cruising grounds. The office was slow, Michael was out, Virginia had a dental appointment. I told John I needed to get some fresh air. That part was true. Once inside the Ramble, I spotted a middle-aged bald guy built like a brick shithouse as they say. He was in leather chaps leaning against a huge bolder, his hand on his crotch squeezing the boner inside his raunchy ripped blue jeans. It's all a favorite fantasy of mine. I followed him into the bushes and knelt on the grass at his feet. I serviced him well. He hugged me tight before I parted. We never spoke. Back at the office John chuckled warmly. He knows me so well. "So, Miles, you had a little dessert, eh?"

Thursday October 7, 1982

I was really looking forward to group therapy tonight. I needed to discuss my trip to the Ramble with the group before I told Abbey about it. Terrence asked me to go first.

"So Miles, tell us how you feel about your trip to the Ramble yesterday."

I'm conflicted. I loved it, yes, I absolutely loved it, the sex was phenomenal. But later on I felt like I betrayed Abbey.

"What do you think Abbey will say?" I'm not sure. Actually, I do, I'm almost certain he won't have a problem with it, at least not as a single episode. He will probably turn it around and give me an equally hot blowjob. He's incredible. I'm so lucky. I'm just a little disappointed in how easily I gave in.

Terrence jumped in. "The lesson here, for all of us, including me, is that we all as gay men have a choice to make regarding casual anonymous sex. Yes or no. Neither is the right answer. It's asking the question that matters most. How will your actions impact others you love? Answer that question first, honestly from your heart, and then let go, be yourself, have fun one way or the other. But please, be in control and always play safe."

Terrence gave me a hug. I felt a whole lot better. I couldn't wait to get home to tell Abbey everything. I was so relieved. I knew Abbey would be fine.

Graham reported that he and Peter invited Glenda out to the Pines as their house guest. Glenda was a huge hit. Not only was she a great cook, she loves disco dancing and is very comfortable around gay men. She had guys rolling on the floor with her dirty jokes. She and Peter had a chance to really talk during long ocean walks. Peter was finally feeling comfortable with having both Graham and Glenda in his life. Glenda made it happen.

178

Eric reported that he and Aaron met Steve and Gordon at the bar Crew's Quarters upstairs in the Pines. After a few beers they all wanted an orgy back at the bungalow on Neptune. However everyone was aware of Terrance's rule that forbids sex between group members. After a lively general discussion, everyone agreed the rule clearly did not apply to Gordon or Aaron. So those two lucky guys tried out the sling in the living room, while Eric and Steve cheered them on from the leather sofa.

Darko missed group. Terrence reported he and Jerry went on a mini-vacation to Boston. Back next week.

Brandon reported his house sitting at One Christopher Street ends in three weeks. Brandon can't go back to the apartment he shared with Jason for eight years. That chapter is closed. It belongs to Jason. Stanley wants Brandon to move in with him. Brandon wonders if they should look for a new apartment together, so they both feel it belongs to both of them. But the housing market is crazy. Prices are at a peak high. Meanwhile, Brandon has been spending more time in Stanley's two-bedroom apartment in the Beresford on Central Park West. He's starting to warm up to the idea. Afterall, the Beresford is one of the top pre-war landmark buildings in Manhattan. Stanley's apartment on the sixth floor faces Central Park. The group laughed. "Please, give us a break. You'd have to be crazy not to take the offer seriously."

Steve reported that he's looking forward to the day he leaves group, so that he and Eric can consummate oral sex at Neptune. Eric's face turned red. The group erupted in laughter. Steve finally gave Eric a hug as he squeezed Eric's gorgeous basket.

FRIDAY OCTOBER 8, 1982

Abbey's favorite cousin Judy came down to the loft for dinner. I made my usual, pasta carbonara. She's great. She loved the loft, the "artsy" feel. She really tuned into the Roman vaulted ceiling. When Jim and I first moved in I started scraping peeled paint off the shallow ceiling vaults. The plaster underneath was this rich deep mustard color that looked just like the buildings you see all over Rome. Just gorgeous. So I scraped the entire ceiling and bought a half dozen photographer's uplights to show it off.

After dinner we took Judy on a short walking tour of the Financial District. A choral concert was going on inside Grace Cathedral at the foot of Wall Street. We could hear the faint sound in the street out front. I love the dark stone walls of the cathedral, blackened from decades of soot. They have so much character; like a black hooded monk kneeling in prayer. I hope they never clean it.

SATURDAY OCTOBER 9, 1982

After the Ramble incident a few days ago, Abbey suggested we pay it another visit together at night. He thought that might be the best way to wrap up the whole affair. I fully agreed. It was dark by the time we arrived. I started looking for the bald guy I had sex with a few days ago. I quickly found the giant bolder. A leatherman in chaps was leaning against it, just like what I'd seen a few days ago. I whispered "I think this could be the guy." We both approached him. I went first as he loosened his belt and fly for us. Amazing. It had to be the same cock. I passed it over to Abbey. He took his time. We traded off half a dozen times. Abbey jerked him off in the end. The three of us group hugged. Abbey asked him for his number. He handed him a black business card with simple white lettering: "Helmut 782-244-2625"

On the walk back home I felt even closer to Abbey. He was absolutely right. The shared sex made everything perfect. Abbey kept looking at the card from Helmut. Stopping at a payphone on Broadway, Abbey was studying the key pad carefully. After a minute he started smiling, then I heard a little chuckle, followed by real laughter. He showed me the card. "Look Miles, the phone numbers spell out the letters SUC-BIG-COCK. All together it reads Helmut SUC-BIG-COCK." Now that's a keeper! You never know when that card might come in handy.

180

As we walked in silence I kept thinking about Helmut and his card. Could I know him from my past somehow? Yes, I must, but from where? He's so familiar. Now I remember it distinctly. Yes, his name was German. It might have been Helmut. It was in the subway tearoom at Bloomingdale's back in winter, maybe February, long before Abbey. Now I remember, it was just a few days after Jim left me. Right around the time I started seeing Terrence. I was out of my mind at the time. My low point.

I had sex with Helmut twice in one day in the same tearoom. He was built like a brick shithouse. I was crazy. We had incredible oral sex. I blew him both times. I couldn't get enough. He had the perfect cock. First time was over my lunch hour, then I returned the same day after work, hoping to find him again. I lucked out. He was still there. He asked me to blow him again. He said I was a great cocksucker. I told him he had the most beautiful cock in the world. I wanted him to somehow save me, take me home, make me his sex slave.

It wasn't rational. I was all alone. My whole world was shattered. I was desperate. Helmut was older and wiser. He felt like a father. He must have understood everything without asking a question. As we parted he handed me a black card with his name and number. Sure enough, when Abbey and I got home to the loft I found Helmut's first card in the box on my desk. Black with white lettering, 782-244-2625. It matched the card Abbey had just received.

SUNDAY OCTOBER 10, 1982

Michael had a pair of extra tickets to the New York City Ballet tonight in Lincoln Center. He offered them to Abbey and me. Very nice. They were doing a favorite Balanchine ballet, Jewels, in three parts Emeralds, Rubies and Diamonds. It's an early abstract ballet. The dancers were fantastic.

During intermission Michael took us into the Green Room to meet his "friend" Philip Johnson, the famous closeted architect. As Michael approached the master, Philip muttered loud enough so I could hear, "Do

I know you?" How embarrassing. That's Michael. Well meaning, but so inappropriate.

Monday October 11, 1982

Robert from the Saint called to review my design for his new house in P-town. The preliminary cost estimate was within his budget. We discussed details and color choices. Robert wanted the floors to be a dark wood, with everything else white inside and out. Color should come from the artwork, oriental rugs and the furnishings. Robert gave me photos and dimensions of all the artwork.

I'm looking into contractors. Robert is a perfectionist like me and we will need an exceptional contractor if the house is to be a success.

Construction documents will go out to bid in five weeks. Robert told me he loved the design, but in his typical manner, he showed no emotion. I'm confident that will change once the actual building starts to take shape before his eyes.

Tuesday October 12, 1982

In tonight's painting class Daniel asked us to paint an abstraction using only blocks of color with minimal line work, focusing on color relationships. He showed numerous examples by Josef Albers and Hans Hofmann that explored the interaction between different colors. It's called color induction. It was interesting to see what different paintings came out of the class. Some had crisp hard edges like the Albers, others had soft messy edges more like the Hofmann. I fell more into the Hofmann camp.

Wednesday October 13, 1982

I called up Jim in San Francisco to wish him an early happy birthday and see how he was doing. Not great. He and Sandy are finished. Jim has found a job with Wells Fargo as the chief editor of the bank's employee newsletter. Certainly below his qualifications, but he can't be picky. At least he has an income. He spends most of his time in gay bars in the Castro looking for Mr. Right. He actually sounds quite happy. He totally loves living in the Castro. He only leaves it for work. He really has a ghetto mentality. He asked about Abbey and how things were going on that front. I told him we were now living together 24/7. He was thrilled.

THURSDAY OCTOBER 14, 1982

This was my 19th group therapy session with Terrence and the guys.

Graham and Peter are in Rome for one week.

Eric and Aaron have become regular members of the main house on Beach Hill. The guys took a vote and it was unanimous to let them in. So they all have meals together, share chores, swim in the pool together and most importantly use the "Sex Shack" 24/7. The only exception being Graham and Eric can never so much as touch. It's pretty wild.

Steve and Gordon had a quiet weekend keeping to themselves. They were holed up in Neptune. The sling is still in the closet. But they weren't playing chess. Just nonstop cocksucking, this time around in bed. Something about Neptune has gotten to them. Maybe it's too dark. Terrence spoke up. "Believe me, it's Neptune. That house has seen more than its share of raunchy dungeon sex over the decades. I never saw such sexual abandon as at those S&M parties in the 70s. Guys going at it everywhere you turned—a nonstop orgy. The owners, a leather couple, ran a 24/7 brothel. Maybe you two need to find another house."

Darko and Jerry just got back from Boston. They had a great get-away. They behaved themselves, just like a straight married couple.

Brandon reported that he will be moving into the Beresford with Stanley this coming week. Stanley is ecstatic. Brandon finally agreed the Beresford is about as good as it gets in New York City. Some guys have all the luck. Brandon deserves a break. He's really a nice guy.

I recapped to the group about my impulsive solo daytrip to the Ramble, followed by my confession to Abbey and the subsequent night visit with Abbey three days later. I had great sex with Helmut both times and Abbey fit right into the threesome so naturally. The group was a bit stunned. Terrence asked "How do you feel about it now." I told them I was fine, completely happy, that Abbey and I have never been closer. I am so proud of how Abbey turned the situation around. He treated me and Helmut with love and complete respect. The three of us bonded as brothers. We may well call up Helmut sometime to share a meal together and get to know each other better. Terrence responded positively. "I'm very impressed Miles. Congratulations to you and Abbey. You should be proud. You both showed courage, maturity and love." We hugged.

FRIDAY OCTOBER 15, 1982

What a pleasant surprise! Out of the blue, I got a major promotion at Michael's office today. I will be named the design junior partner. My salary will double overnight. Michael is parting with his Canadian partner in Toronto and will be in New York City full time as the senior partner. Another young man from Canada named Paul will become Michael's business junior partner. It's an honor for someone my age. I think Michael did it to make sure I don't walk away. Whatever. Plus Michael wants to move the office into larger, more professional quarters. The new firm name will be Arch Plus. So, all's good for the time being. We all celebrated together with dinner at the Rainbow Room: Michael and his girlfriend Marsha, Paul with his German wife Gretta and Abbey and me, the two creative queers. We all danced together as if we were in the Pines Pavilion.

SUNDAY OCTOBER 17, 1982

Last minute, we decided to celebrate my job promotion and take the seaplane out to the Pines for the weekend. We booked the best room at the Botel, which isn't much, but it's the only hotel in the Pines. Saturday we had salmon dinners at the Monster in Cherry Grove and afterwards returned in the water taxi. We danced for hours in the Pines Pavilion with cute sweaty guys. The Pines is getting really nice and quiet. Most of the renters have left already. The homeowners are returning to visit with their old friends and close up their houses for the season. The ocean is still warm, the fall colors are beautiful. The Rack is empty. Sunday we walked to Water Island, which was even quieter than the Pines.

MONDAY OCTOBER 18, 1982

I was coming home from work at the 72nd Street C Station. I needed to pee. I popped into the men's room off the subway platform. I had heard it was an active tearoom since it serves the Ramble nearby. It had been months since I got any of that hot tearoom sex. I scored. Inside at the urinals, three guys with their backs to me were jerking off. As I got nearer, the one on the end turned towards me. It was Angelo from my painting class! His hardon in clear view was a 10. I had always suspected it would be. Embarrassed, he blushed red. I quickly asked him, "Are you alright? Want some head? Relax." As a smile gradually filled his face, Angelo surrendered his beautiful Florentine cock to me.

TUESDAY OCTOBER 19, 1982

Daniel told us to paint anything at all, but it must be something you love. That was easy. Angelo's cock. I decided to do one of my quadrant cock paintings so I could be more expressive. Just the torso. I didn't want anyone besides Angelo to know whose cock I was painting. Four distinct cock views in four distinct colors—blue, pink, orange and red. It was easy to paint since I now knew it so intimately. God, what a gorgeous Italian cock. It made me think back on my Venetian gondolier and my Catholic priest. I missed them both. Italian men really do have superior cocks. No question about it. Of course, Daniel loved the painting. Angelo looked at it carefully when I was finished. "Bellisimo!" Before parting from Angelo, I invited him to dinner Friday at the loft. I want Abbey to meet him.

Wednesday October 20, 1982

Simon called tonight. He sounded great. He loves the new job at Der Scutt. He congratulated me on being made a partner. He told me he's put the Mine Shaft on the back burner. It's too dangerous. Guys are getting sick. He was tested two weeks ago. He's negative thank God. Yesterday he went by GMHC. He's decided to join their Buddy Program. Wow! I congratulated him.

Thursday October 21, 1982

It's my 20th session of GT. A milestone.

Graham reported that he and Peter had a perfect Roman holiday. Beautiful weather and even more beautiful Roman men. Peter wants to move permanently. He sounds serious. He's got an old college friend who works at the Rome Stock Exchange. They are talking. Graham is a little concerned.

Eric and Aaron continue to comingle with those in the main house on Beach Hill. On Saturday night they had Terry and Bob out to the cottage for a foursome. It must be the attraction of something new, "fresh meat." The season is winding down and some guys are feeling a little desperate to find a partner for the coming winter.

Darko and Jerry had a quiet Saturday going in Brooklyn Heights, until Jerry returned from the Promenade with Franco, a cute Italian bank employee who's into anal sex. He stayed the night and they all had brunch together at a trendy new place on Montague Street on Sunday. Franco is adorable with his broken English. I stayed mute.

Steve reported that he and Gordon looked at small beach shacks to rent in the Pines. They liked something simple on Cedar Walk with lots of glass and a bright sunny interior. The opposite of Neptune. It's only available for four weeks, until Thanksgiving, when the pipes are drained for the winter. They signed a lease immediately.

Brandon announced that he and Stanley are throwing a party for the entire group plus Terrence on Sunday afternoon in Stanley's apartment in the Beresford. It's their way of celebrating their new relationship. The group gave Brandon a standing ovation.

I mentioned my job promotion and celebration in the Pines with Abbey. I told them Simon joined the GMHC Buddy Program.

FRIDAY OCTOBER 22, 1982

Angelo came down to the loft for dinner. He loved the loft ceiling that looks like Rome. He's such a sweet guy. He and Abbey hit it off immediately, exchanging jokes and hand gestures. We served him my pasta carbonara, which he politely said was delicious, as if it compared to the real thing he was used to in Italy. I showed him my slides of Florence taken during my Cornell summer program nine years ago. I was impressed; Angelo identified everyone. Afterwards Abbey asked him if he'd like to have a little fun. He said, "Bene, buono, bene!" Abbey said "Just relax and let us take care of you. You are our guest." I told him I'd really love to hold his beautiful Italian cock again. Abbey and I undressed Angelo nice and slow. He looked like an ancient Roman athlete. We lovingly serviced every square inch of him. Pure adoration. Afterwards we showered, and went for an evening walking tour of the Financial District.

SATURDAY OCTOBER 23, 1982

Abbey and I spent most of the day at the Metropolitan Museum of Art on Upper Fifth Avenue. It was the first visit in six months. Last April Helmut had showed me their collection of ancient marble Greek and Roman athletes. It felt so good to be back. I love this museum.

SUNDAY OCTOBER 24, 1982

I invited Patrick down to the Bennett Building to sample my pasta carbonara. He's doing much better. We've become best friends. He also knows Abbey well. After the meal we all relaxed on the big bed, telling

187

stories, making ourselves comfortable. One thing led to another. Abbey gave Patrick a gentle body massage. I could see Patrick was getting aroused. He told us he misses sex with men. It's been years. I decided to take the plunge. "You know Patrick, maybe we can do something about that right now." I put my hand on his basket and gently fondled his stiffening cock. His free hand on top of mine asked for more. "Patrick, please fuck me using a condom." "I would really love to Miles. I tuned into your butt the moment you walked into the Ramrod." "It's all yours Buddy, I can see you're a real stud. I handed him a condom. Patrick started off real slow. Soon he was on fire. It was his first sex with another man in years. It was pure therapy. He turned into a West Village leatherman before our eyes. We both shed tears while Abbey mussed our hair. I gave Patrick my warmest hug. "From now on Patrick I'll call you My Prince."

MONDAY OCTOBER 25, 1982

Big news in the office. Arch Plus was awarded the contract to design a new elementary school on Roosevelt Island for the city. Michael is thrilled. We'll have to hire staff. Good thing our new office space will be ready by mid-November. It's all terribly exciting. We made it into the Big League. It's a great early birthday present.

TUESDAY OCTOBER 26, 1982

I turned 32 today. It has been quite a year so far. First Venice, then Jim walked out on me, then four months of heaven and hell searching for Mr. Right, finally finding my new beloved Abbey, then being made a partner at work. It's all been so amazing. What a year so far.

I missed my painting class tonight. We're out celebrating with Bob and Dave. Dinner at The Four Seasons, my absolute favorite restaurant in the city. Everything was perfect. Angie joined us. It's like dining in heaven. Back home in the loft we had XXX birthday sex. Abbey showed me the stars.

Wednesday October 27, 1982

As I was finishing the dinner dishes, the phone rang. Abbey picked up. It was Jim. I got on the second phone. Jim sounded absolutely incredible. First, he wished me a belated happy birthday. He could hardly contain himself. "I want you to say hello to someone very special. This is my new sweetheart, Philip Turner." We were speechless. Then suddenly, this strong booming voice came across the line, "Well, how the hell are you? Jim can't stop talking about you two, so I said let's just call these fellas up and introduce me. So, again, how the hell are you?" Philip had Abbey and me rolling on the floor. That was Philip, Jim's new beau. He sounded wonderful. What a switch from Sandy. Philip is from Oklahoma, tall and lanky, queer as a three-dollar bill, a real ball buster, a CPA in charge of the books for a major Mexican restaurant in the Tenderloin, and he's head-over-heels in love with "Jimmy." We were thrilled. Jim insisted we fly out for Thanksgiving. Absolutely, we put it on the calendar. What good news!

Thursday October 28, 1982

Tonight will be group therapy session #21. Lots to report.

Graham was not his usual calm self. Terrence asked immediately, "Are you alright?" "No, I'm a wreck." Peter applied for a position with the Rome Stock Exchange and passed the first phone interview. Next they are flying Peter to Rome tomorrow for more senior level interviews. It all sounds very serious. Peter has lost all his marbles over living in Rome. Nothing Graham says anymore matters. Peter expects Graham to follow him, find a new job as an accountant in Rome. Graham said he doesn't want to leave his New York City job which he loves. He was recently promoted. Graham is worried the relationship is over. The group was stunned. Terrence cautioned Graham that the situation was beyond his control. "Be prepared to let go."

Eric and Aaron bonded with Terry and Bob. Apparently the sex they all shared together in the Sex Cottage was so hot, they plan to do a repeat performance this weekend. They're on fire! Terrence cautioned Eric that the situation was not sustainable. "Eventually, you both will have to face reality." "No thanks, we can handle it." "Good luck. Make sure you play safe."

Darko and Jerry have also really bonded with Jerry's Italian pickup Franco. He's just lonely. He cruises the Promenade hoping to be picked up. He's a bottom with a sexy Italian butt. It all sounds so familiar. Anyway, Darko told the group that he and Jerry gave Franco an open invitation to drop by anytime he's lonely.

Steve reported that he and Gordon love the new sun-filled house on Cedar. They have met their elder neighbors and have many things in common. When they learned Steve and Gordon were coming from the shack on Neptune, their eyes opened wide. "Really, no kidding. Is it true they have a sex sling in the living room?"

Brandon reported the party in the Beresford was a hit. The group gave him a standing ovation. Towards the end of the evening Stanley apparently sang show tunes at his Steinway baby grand. Brandon oversaw the gay caterer who was very cute. His name is Chloe. Apparently he's the hottest ticket in town these days, a rock star. All his staff have gym bods and Chloe dresses them bare chested in just leather vests and hot pants. I'm really sorry Abbey and I missed the party. Brandon and Stanley are looking into a winter getaway in the Caribbean, possibly Little Dix Bay.

I finished by telling the group about Patrick's visit and our sex scene. The group was split. Conservative guys like Brandon thought sex with guys who have AIDS was wrong. They think it's dangerous and irresponsible. Liberal guys like Abbey and me or possibly Steve or Eric think AIDS and sex can co-exist as long as safe sex is strictly observed. Guys with AIDS have sex drives just like the rest of us, often even hotter. They can make wonderful lovers. They often have gained greater insight by facing death directly. I got a warm group hug.

Before we broke up Terrence had a special topic he wanted to discuss with the group. Over the weekend he and his Black lover Thomas were the victims of a hate crime. They were leaving the New St. Marks Baths late after an evening of fun together. They were holding hands laughing, stealing a kiss, when three white punks confronted them yelling homophobic epithets, pushing Thomas to the ground, kicking him repeatedly in the chest and leaving him bleeding in the street. All the while they were yelling homophobic insults: "cocksuckers, faggots, butt fuckers, butt boys." Terrence took Thomas to the emergency room at St. Vincent's. They spent the night there. Fortunately, no ribs were broken. The whole incident left Terrence very shaken up. The group was stunned. Everyone needed to give Terrence a hug. Most guys were on the verge of tears. Regaining his composure, Terrence said he had an assignment for next week's group therapy. He passed out handouts labeled "Shame or Pride?" Next to a list of each of our names he had put a commonly used homophobic epithet. Our assignment was to discuss each word. How does it make you feel? If you feel shame, can you turn it around to feel pride? What a great assignment. Here was Terrence's list: Miles – cocksucker / Brandon – poofter / Steve – butt-boy / Darko – faggot / Eric – pervert / Graham – butt-fucker

FRIDAY OCTOBER 29, 1982

Abbey and I were hot to see Paul Newman's new movie The Verdict. God, he's so sexy with his baby blues. He plays a Boston lawyer looking for redemption. Reminded me a little of myself, best intentions, but always chasing cock.

SATURDAY OCTOBER 30, 1982

Abbey and I did the Saint again Saturday night. It was their annual Black Party. A very hot ticket. It's an international gay circuit event. Robert got us in free as his guests on his gold membership. He joined us for a bit, but he left before midnight, before it got really raunchy. It was packed solid with over 4,000 guys mostly in elaborate leather costumes, lots of chiseled flesh in leather harnesses, kinky live sex acts on raised platforms, oiled muscle men all mixed together with a heavy disco beat. A bit like a Fellini gay orgy, set in ancient Rome. The sex balcony was particularly busy. We ran into Andrei, the young Romanian surgeon-in-training in skimpy leather shorts and a harness. He was on his way to the balcony, of course.

SUNDAY OCTOBER 31, 1982

Abbey and I both woke up late with a pair of stiff morning glories. It was past 2:00 pm in the afternoon. We enjoyed some raunchy sex. It was brought on by the Black Party last night. What total debauchery. It made the Mine Shaft look like kindergarten. Head-to-toe Leathermen screwing everywhere you looked. Maybe it's time to give the Saint a rest, you think?

MONDAY NOVEMBER 1, 1982

Back in the office Monday morning Michael wanted all the juicy details from the Saint. For a supposedly straight man, he seems awfully interested in the gay scene. Plus his fixation on ballet and opera. Sure he has a girlfriend, Marsha, but that could just be a cover and they aren't even married. Anyway, he definitely wants to meet Abbey, so we're invited to dinner Saturday night. He lives on Central Park West about fifteen blocks up from Bob and Dave's. It's on a high floor. Barbara Streisand lives directly over him. Maybe she'll come down and sing us a tune. Dream on.

TUESDAY NOVEMBER 2, 1982

Today was our last painting class with Daniel. Boy, those eight weeks really flew by fast. Daniel brought in a boxful of assorted Italian pastries from Rocco's. Even Angelo was impressed. For our last painting session together Daniel asked us to paint each other, singularly, or as a pair or as the whole group. That was easy. I painted Angelo and Daniel.

My vertical painting was a surrealist take-off on your traditional Italian Annunciation with the two parts—an angel Angelo, appearing in a garden in the left half and the Virgin Mary Daniel, standing in a loggia in the right half. What was unusual in my version was the gay subtext. Angelo and Daniel are presented as gay lovers, shown at the moment of their

192

consummation. They are scantily clad in white silk groin cloths. Their eyes meet for the first time, revealing their mutual devotion. Through the gathered silk folds we can make out a pair of enormous erect cocks spewing out tiny white droplets of cum reaching up into heaven. At the top of the painting is the heavenly Father looking down, his parted arms giving the lovers his final blessing. Angelo and Daniel both wanted the painting. Daniel politely gave in.

WEDNESDAY NOVEMBER 3, 1982

What an extraordinary gift. In today's mail a large cubic box arrived, post marked San Francisco. Inside, buried in a dozen pieces of crumpled newspaper and bubble wrap was a precious porcelain tea bowl from Jim. I recognized it immediately and gasped. It was one of two tea bowls Jim had from his revered ceramic's teacher at Princeton, Toshiko Takaezu. It has a most astonishing cobalt blue glaze, her trade secret. I had met Toshiko in Ithaca when Jim invited her to give a master class at Cornell. She is a National Living Treasure. I was deeply touched. Jim didn't even include a note. He didn't have to. This was his way of telling me how much he loved me.

THURSDAY NOVEMBER 4, 1982

Tonight is group therapy session #22. It's going to be extra special. Not business as usual. Terrence gave us an assignment concerning homophobic epithets. I get to go first for a change.

My name was paired up with the word "cocksucker." That's me for sure. I'm a proud card-carrying cocksucker. A perfect 6. There was never any real shame, just curiosity. Even at age five I sort of knew it, back in the men's locker room at the public pool in Albuquerque. I wasn't sucking yet, but I was sure looking. In college I'd finally got my first taste. I'd say it's God's greatest gift to mankind. I feel sorry for all those uptight straight men who haven't tried it. It seems so natural. I'm just a proud cocksucker. I suspect we all are.

Brandon went next. He was paired with the word "poofter." He laughed. Poofter is a term he uses with Stanley all the time. Since the word has a British derivation, Brandon is partial to the term. He loves it! Afterall, his ancestors came over on the Mayflower.

Steve was up next with the phrase "butt boy." First, he announced unapologetically, "I'm a proud top anal guy. I used to always be on the lookout for a good butt boy. But now I'm blessed. Gordon is my perfect 'butt boy.' I adore him. Nothing gives me greater pleasure. He wears a dark blue bandana in his left rear pocket just to remind me how much he loves me. That's the way we see it—butt fucker and butt boy." On the shame vs. pride question, he said he's 100% unashamed. The group gave Steve a standing ovation complete with whoops and hollers.

Darko was paired with the word "faggot." He was uncomfortable from the get-go. It all went back to his tearoom days. Several times he had gotten beaten badly by homophobes in tearooms. They would yell at him, mocking him over and over, "Take that you faggot." Terrence hugged Darko until he calmed down.

Eric discussed the word "pervert." He could take it or leave it. It doesn't offend him. He knows he's different, so what. It's his business. He enjoys it all, top or bottom. "All these labels are a pile of crap. We're just men who love men." That line brought down the house.

Graham went last with "butt-fucker." He identifies with the label. He's a proud top. Peter is his "butt boy." He knows how to take it "up the ass." Graham and Peter are totally unashamed of both labels. It's plain and simple. It just means Graham knows how to make love to Peter properly. And we all know Peter has a gorgeous derriere. Graham's proud of his sex skills.

Terrence wrapped things up. He was impressed at how confident and proud we all are of our sexuality. "You youngsters are leading the way into the future. God bless you."

FRIDAY NOVEMBER 5, 1982

Jim's buddy from Princeton, Gordon, called out of the blue. He's passing through New York City and wants to see me and finally meet Abbey. He heard all about Jim's new boyfriend Philip. How about dinner in Chinatown? I suggested we include upstairs Douglas. Great! Gordon loves Douglas. He suggested we all have a little sex afterwards. I finally got to get my hands around Gordon's cock while he wore his hot bomber jacket.

SATURDAY NOVEMBER 6, 1982

Abbey and I had dinner Saturday night at Michael and Marsha's, way up on CPW. One of those huge pre-war brick piles; on a high floor in a doorman building. Michael bought it decades ago for peanuts; now it's probably worth over a million. I told Abbey we're wearing our full black leather. It's sort of a test. Michael is a character and a half. He talked nonstop, he's very insecure, but he always means well. He should have been a stand-up comedian. He's as funny as Jack Benny. Loves to poke fun at himself. Thinks nothing of falling on the floor in his custom-made suit if it will get him a laugh. Marsha was just the opposite, soft spoken, reserved, a bit shy. I really liked her. I'm sort of her equivalent. She shares his bed; I share his office. He desperately needs both of us.

Michael has a terrible habit of name-dropping and telling white lies. It's gone on for so long, that at this point, he believes them himself. Mostly harmless. I play along; I try to outdo him. He tells me he knows Barbara Streisand intimately. "Oh, did you know Abbey and Barry Manilow dated for over a month?" Michael is always trying to impress me. As if that will cement my loyalty to him. I admire his devotion to his two sons from his first marriage. He clearly adores them. I think he sees me as a third.

At the apartment door on the way out, he insisted on trying on my worn black leather motorcycle jacket. It fit him perfectly. He actually looked quite hot in it. "Okay, Michael, let's hand over the goods, you sexy stud." I finally got him to laugh.

SUNDAY NOVEMBER 7, 1982

Patrick told me he likes phone sex. It's safe. Guys don't freak out over the AIDS thing. He asked me to call him sometime when I'm feeling super-horny. "Just say you're my butt-boy. I'll know it's you. I'll be your Prince Patrick."

I've been thinking about Patrick all weekend. I decided to call him up this morning. Try out a little phone sex.

"Hello Patrick. Is your cock in your hand? This is your butt-boy. How is my Prince? Ready to fuck me again? I miss your big Irish dick up my ass."

"Get your tight Italian butt over here. On the double, you slut. I'm gonna fuck you blindfolded. Remember, I'm your Prince."

"Yes Sir."

MONDAY NOVEMBER 8, 1982

My British architect friend John is leaving Arch Plus, headed back to the UK. I'll miss him. He's my closest straight friend in New York City. He has a wonderful dry sense of humor, very English. He'll be in London when Abbey and I visit around Christmas. He wants to get together. He recommended a small hotel in Bloomsbury called Repton House.

TUESDAY NOVEMBER 9, 1982

I invited my painting instructor Daniel down for dinner in the loft. Abbey wants to meet him. I did the usual pasta carbonara. Daniel won't mind. He told me he can't boil water. We mostly talked about my painting. He was encouraging me to keep it up. He thinks I have natural talent. Whatever, I just paint. I showed him my most recent butt painting, the one I did late at night. It shows four guy's gorgeous plump butts skimpily clad. Daniel loved it, of course. He wants to buy it. The painting somehow got us on the topic of Angelo. Daniel has a major crush on him. I told him about our recent threesome several weeks ago. Daniel was instantly jealous. Abbey spoke up. "Nonsense Daniel. We can arrange another with you, no problem. Angelo will be interested for sure. Meanwhile, let's have some fun here, right now. You've got a gorgeous butt yourself. Would you be interested?" Daniel blushed, but immediately volunteered, "Sure, I'm a bottom."

WEDNESDAY NOVEMBER 10, 1982

After dinner tonight my brother Mark called. He wants us to meet his new girlfriend Tam. She is a student of his at RISD. Mark has been teaching an architectural design studio to seniors two days a week. He commutes back and forth to Providence. It gives him a chance to see Terry and Edward, plus my sister and her husband. Mark sounded great. New love. Dinner at his loft next Wednesday.

THURSDAY NOVEMBER 11, 1982

Tonight is group therapy session #23 with Terrence and the guys. I'm excited.

Brandon said he and Stanley feel like a new chapter is opening up in their lives. They are talking to a lawyer about child adoption. There is a ton of paperwork and a dozen hurdles, but they are both up for the challenge. The group was terribly impressed. Terrence congratulated Brandon and Stanley. He offered his help in any way possible.

Graham looked pale. He could barely speak. Peter accepted a job offer from the Rome Stock Exchange. He leaves on Saturday. Graham is staying in New York City; their six-month relationship is over. Terrence gave Graham a hug. The news left the group silent and a little depressed.

Eric reported next weekend will be he and Aaron's final Pines visit of the season. They both regret they didn't spend more time and energy cultivating friendships to enjoy over the long winter. Seems like all they did was fuck their brains out with faceless strangers. Terrence said, "Don't be too hard on yourselves. This is a common lesson many Pines men learn during their first summer."

Darko reported that Franco had returned to Italy. His bank assignment was over. They are feeling depressed with winter on the horizon. Darko is thinking of taking a Chinese cooking class at a restaurant on Montague Street. Jerry is bored. He's been hanging out in tearooms again. Darko doesn't know what to do. Terrence invited Jerry to see him in therapy privately. Darko will discuss this offer with Jerry.

Steve said he and Gordon have only two weekends left in the Pines. They know they need to settle on a renewal for next year. They are both torn between Neptune and Cedar, darkness and raunchy sex or sunshine and a good night's rest. They are pulled both ways.

I reported about Abbey and my threesomes of late with Douglas, Helmut, Angelo, Gordon and Daniel. Were there more? I wasn't even sure. I was curious what the group and Terrence thought of all this fucking around, so to speak. Am I turning into a slut again? Dragging Abbey down with me? I can't seem to help myself.

The group thought Abbey and I generally handled each situation well, keeping communication channels open, taking good care of each other. They didn't think I was a slut. They actually said they admired and respected both Abbey and me. I was deeply touched. Terrence was a bit more skeptical. "Miles, I know you love sex. Abbey seems to love it as well. I truly believe you both find sex to be beautiful and natural. You both seem quite able to share sexual experiences with a new partner, as long as you are both equally involved in the encounter. But you are in unchartered territory. Few couples can negotiate this situation for long. I admire your curiosity, your courage, your capacity to love. Play safe and always act out of love. Talk, talk and then talk some more. I love you." That night I cherished Terrence's words and his embrace more than ever before.

FRIDAY NOVEMBER 12, 1982

I wanted to go to Man's Country with Abbey. I had my reasons. Of course I wanted to see and hear Bette Midler, who performs there regularly, accompanied by Barry Manilow on piano as Bette flings poppers into the crowd. You see, Abbey had a month-long fling with Barry awhile back, long before me. I figured the least he could do is sign a record cover. Actually, he was extremely charming, definitely a heart throb. I could easily see how Abbey fell for him. But he broke my Abbey's heart. I decided a hand shake was good enough. I could skip the autograph.

Since we had already paid for full admission to the baths, we decided to cruise the halls just in case. We scored big time. One partially open door on the top floor revealed a gorgeous butt boy laid out on a perfect white towel. The angel's head was turned away on the white pillow. We closed the door. He was the butt boy of our dreams. The cheeks had crisp dark tan lines from a skimpy bikini that were driving me crazy. Abbey went first, then me. He never turned to face us. Just moans of pure pleasure. Sometime later, we were all pleasantly exhausted. Finally, he turned to show us his face. Super cute with a mischievous grin. His name was Tim; he just turned 18, but he's no virgin that's for sure. New in town from Minnesota. Ran away from his homophobic father. A really sweet kid. "He's the boogie woogie bugle boy of company B."

SUNDAY NOVEMBER 13-14, 1982

At the last minute, we decided to catch the early Saturday morning train to Sayville, headed to the Pines. We called ahead for a room at the Botel. Not necessary. The Pines was empty. That's precisely why we were headed there. The emptiness was romantic. The place was simply gorgeous. Autumn colors, the smell of burning logs, muffled laughter around dinner tables. The tempered Atlantic keeps the air just warm enough for long beach walks. We ran into Steve and Gordon on the beach. They were glad to finally meet

Abbey after hearing so much about him in group. Steve told Abbey, "You should know, this guy here really adores you."

This would be our last visit of 1982. Who knows, maybe next year we'll take the plunge and take a full share in a house for the long season. It's very tempting. It feels like where we belong.

MONDAY NOVEMBER 15, 1982

Robert wanted to review the construction drawings of his new P-town house after work. He's as anal as I am. He went over every detail. It took over two hours. The good news is he changed almost nothing. He wants to upgrade the kitchen and bathroom finishes using polished travertine and natural cherry instead of ceramic tile and plastic laminate. Fine. He has deep pockets. It will look much nicer. Robert is the perfect client.

TUESDAY NOVEMBER 16, 1982

It was move-in day for Arch Plus. I was very proud of the spacious new office in Tribeca which I had designed. Clean, modern, open and very elegant with classic modern pieces of furniture by Mies van der Rohe. What a change from our cramped tight quarters on CPW. Michael was extremely pleased and thanked me for making it happen. Time to hire more staff. Our new landlord was the Catholic Archdiocese of New York. It turns out they own huge tracks of real estate in Lower Manhattan. From my 7th floor windows I had an unobstructed view of Manhattan, the twin towers shimmering in the morning sun.

WEDNESDAY NOVEMBER 17, 1982

After a crazy day at work unpacking, my brother Mark had Abbey and me over to his Soho loft for dinner. His real reason was to meet his new girlfriend Tam. She is a senior student of his at RISD. It's not uncommon for straight men to get involved with their attractive female college students. Gays do as well, but I think far less so. Mark's face was aglow. He's totally in love. Tam is sweet, bubbly, full of life. She's an only child, so

200

she was spoiled rotten growing up in Greenwich, Connecticut. But I liked her immediately. After dinner we played a game of Scrabble. Of course Abbey easily won. As we were leaving, Mark whispered that he and Tam were getting married after New Year's in Connecticut. I'm to be his Best Man. Of course Abbey is invited.

THURSDAY NOVEMBER 18, 1982

Tonight was my 24th session of group with Terrence. He looked exhausted.

Brandon filled us in on the child adoption search. It's very complicated. They are working with a lawyer and two placement agencies. They are hoping to find a single mother willing to sign away her baby right after giving birth. Sounds very difficult, especially for a gay couple. Brandon and Stanley need to be able to hop on a plane at a moment's notice to meet the birth mother and sign papers to release the baby into their care. The mother can back out of the deal up to the last second. That has already happened once in Kansas. It's all very stressful; an emotional rollercoaster. The group wished them the best of luck.

We all knew something was up the moment we saw Graham. First of all, he was wearing a motorcycle jacket for the first time. Plus, in his right rear Levi pocket was a light blue bandana, the clue that signals you give head. He sounded terrific. He told the group he was over Peter and Peter's crazy girlfriend Glenda. Saturday, after Peter left for Rome, he went shopping. In Hudson's he picked up the jacket and a few jock straps. At the Christopher Street Bookstore he picked up a few colored bandanas. Saturday night he wore the new outfit to the Ramrod. His first-time visit. He started talking to this cute young kid at the pool table named Jed. Jed asked him if he'd like a ride on his Harley parked out front. "Sure. Where to?" Jed replied, "I think you're really hot. Let's hit the empty trucks in the Meat Packing District. I saw your bandana. I want you to give me some head. Are you interested?" "Jed, you must have read my mind. Let's get down to it." Well, they did more than just suck cock. Afterwards, Graham took Jed to the Empire Diner for a sunrise breakfast. He spilled his heart out. Jed was a good listener. His advice was simple. "Forget Peter. You're hot. Just have some fun." Terrence interrupted, "So Graham, how did you feel when you heard Jed's advice?" "A little foolish. Jed's just a kid. Super sweet. His needs and mine are completely different. I needed to assert myself after Peter. He hurt me. I thought he loved me. I feel much stronger after my brief encounter with Jed. He really helped me get over Peter." "Good work Graham."

Eric announced that he and Aaron are taking a full share in the main house on Beach Hill next summer. They spoke to the owners and were pleased to hear they will only allow full shares. They want to cultivate relationships, not just turn a lot of tricks.

Darko was pleased to announce that Jerry is starting one-on-one therapy with Terrence to help him get over his tearoom fixation. Meanwhile, Darko is already thinking about Christmas decorations. Thanksgiving is next Thursday and Darko always likes to get started decorating as soon as the turkey leaves the table.

Steve and Gordon finally reached a decision about which house to rent next summer—Cedar, for a good night's rest or Neptune, for sex all night in a sling. Cedar won. The group applauded.

I told the group that Abbey and I are looking into an ad in The Native for a full share in a four-bedroom house in the Pines. It will have four couples whom we'd see every weekend and get to really know. Sounds perfect. One of the owners is a gay attorney in Manhattan, the other owner runs an art gallery on the Upper West Side. They want to interview us next week. They have floor plans. Apparently the design has a Japanese feel. Supposedly, it was designed by an Associate in I.M. Pei and Partners. I was impressed.

SATURDAY NOVEMBER 19-20, 1982

Abbey and I made another Amtrack trip to Providence to visit my family again. It's been four months. It's a pre-Thanksgiving visit since we'll be in

San Francisco for turkey day with Jim and Philip. Normally we all celebrate Thanksgiving at my sister's house. Over the years my visits to Providence follow a pleasant pattern, arriving early on a Friday, lunch with my parents in Saunderstown, usually with a visit to the RISD Art Museum, dinner out at the Lobster Pot overlooking the ocean, maybe a tour of a Newport mansion Saturday morning, some yard work with Edward and then headed back home late afternoon on Amtrack. I enjoy the familiar pattern. There is always something new in the familiar. Edward's cancer is never discussed. Edward, Abbey and I bonded while raking the leaves into giant piles. My sister joined us for the bonfire. Looking into the dancing flames, it always brought us back to childhood. Terry watched from the kitchen window.

Sunday November 21, 1982

On the train back from Providence Abbey and I reminisced about Helmut, the German guy we hooked up with in the Ramble that night over a month ago. We both had fond memories of him. Of course, my roots to Helmut run deeper. He's a father figure. My encounters with Helmut in the subway tearoom right after Jim left me will always touch me deeply. When we called him up Saturday night to propose getting together on Sunday, Helmut proposed one better. Why not meet tonight? That way we'd have the whole night. Helmut explained, he's a night owl, he likes to cruise the city in dark empty places, looking for action in the wee hours. The abandoned yards beneath the elevated highway, at the foot of the Brooklyn Bridge are popular with his leather buddies late into the night. Uninhibited queer sex out in the open, under the cavernous stone vaults, facing the East River.

We met Helmut in front of the Bennett Building at midnight and walked east. Helmut had on the same leather chaps and frayed Levi's that he'd worn to the Ramble and the subway tearoom. I could hear the hum of the overhead traffic through the steel grating on-ramps to the Brooklyn Bridge. Up ahead, under a massive stone vault, we could make out three figures grouped around a tall man standing in the middle. Getting closer, I could see in the moonlight that he was wearing an Army uniform. His trousers had been pulled down, exposing an erection and snowy-white butt in the moonlight.

A handsome black leatherman was tight up against his backside, his hardon up the soldier's white ass. In front, a kneeling dock worker was giving him head with great gusto. The soldier was smiling.

Nearby a James Dean look-alike was paying close attention. He looked like a boxer who had just stepped out of the rink in white silk boxer trunks. Helmut whispered to Abbey and then to me, "The kid is up next." Helmut turned to the kid, planted his outstretched arms on his shoulders and forced him down on his knees. Helmut placed Abbey square in front of the kneeling acolyte. "Take good care of my two buddies. You know what they need." The kid made intense love to Abbey's cock. Then it was my turn. He took me back to my Catholic priest in San Giovanni Grisostomo. Two men so different, the kid and the priest, yet the same.

Afterwards, Abbey and I were feeling completely drained, quite content to just sit on the sideline in each other's arms, a couple of voyeurs. Time was suspended. New faces arrived, new bodies came and went. All seeking release in this outdoor arena of queer sex.

Of course, the kid eventually ended up on the center stage, his boxer trunks at his ankles. Helmut claimed his prize. The raw male sex, captured in the silver moonlight, was hauntingly beautiful. Abbey and I said good night to Helmut and his buddies. We walked away in silence, back to the loft. It was almost 3:30 am.

MONDAY NOVEMBER 22, 1982

Just another day. Why are some days frozen in time? Like the afternoon on the school playground, the afternoon when John Fitzgerald Kennedy was shot in Dallas, Texas. We were told to come inside and sit still in our desks. While my teacher, Ms. Williams, wept openly. I recall that painful moment precisely. Every detail is sharp in focus. It never fades like all the other memories. Even lover's faces fade, no matter how hard we try to recall them, the precise color of their eyes, as they silently approach to plant a precious kiss on our lips.

Tuesday November 23, 1982

Tonight is the foursome with Daniel, Angelo, Abbey and me that we promised Daniel a week ago. Daniel has a crush on Angelo. We didn't mention this fact to Angelo; he'll find out soon enough. Plus, Daniel confided he's strictly a bottom. I'm almost certain Angelo is strictly a top. Aren't most Italians? It's so complicated.

Why is it that so many gay guys have such narrowly defined sex roles? Strictly top or strictly bottom. Not like me. Boy was I lucky. My first gay lover was a hippie flower child named Johnny; almost a decade ago, back in Ithaca, back in college. I was a virgin. Johnny was an experienced sex guru. He had exotic sex manuals with diagrams of dozens of positions for queer sex. Johnny taught me them all, one-by-one. He showed me how to relax, how to communicate with a lover so that each of us achieved maximum pleasure. All this during one long steamy night of nonstop sex. Johnny was tremendous.

Wednesday November 24, 1982

Abbey and I are off to San Francisco for a week over Thanksgiving. Of course, we are staying with Jim and Philip in their new apartment on Dolores Street in the Mission District. It's my first visit to San Francisco. Abbey lived there in 1972 for six-months on Polk Street in the Tenderloin, until his money ran out. Jim and Philip are the perfect couple. Head-over-heels in love. Jim has become "Jimmy." Philip, tall and lanky, has this charming rural twang that screams Oklahoma. Beware if someone tries to give him trouble, out comes his long leg with a pointed cowboy boot planted square in their balls.

The Castro is pretty wild. Everywhere you turn there are gorgeous Marlboro Men with thick black bushy moustaches, gleaming white teeth, and of course, they are all shirtless with chiseled chests and six-pack abs. Baskets that leave me faint. Everyone is super friendly. Always on the lookout for a quick hookup. I couldn't refuse a few offers.

Thursday November 25, 1982

Thanksgiving. I have so much to be thankful for. Abbey, the new center of my life, the most wonderful partner on earth, my future, and Jim with Philip, my cherished center from the past and my best friends. The two parts now joined as one. I am a happy man.

Friday November 26, 1982

Jim and Philip gave us the in-depth tour of the Castro, America's #1 gay ghetto. Everything about the Castro was gay: the famous book store, the even more famous camera shop, the florist, the travel agency with photos of sexy guys in skimpy Speedos in the window, the cookie outlet, the bank, the sex shops, the cookbook store, the queer art gallery, the historic movie theater, the 24/7 restaurants, the drag queen barber, the grocer with the full basket to go. Get the picture? And the men, my God. It was overwhelming. Good thing we don't live here. I'd have trouble holding down a job with all these cute guys eyeing me over on every street corner. I'd never make it into the office. Jim took it all in stride, as if this was all normal. This is definitely not normal.

Jim wanted to show us the Castro Theatre from the 1920s with its towering Churrigueresque façade right in the heart of the Castro. It's the ultimate movie palace. We went in to see Bette Davis in Now, Voyager. When the lights went up Jim pointed out the local celebrity, Armistead Maupin, seated in the row in front of us. He's the author of the hit serial Tales of the City.

In the evening they gave us a tour of the dozens of gay bars, many with cute go-go boy strippers dancing nearly nude in well-packaged jock straps on the bar countertops, ten-dollar bills spilling out from their soft pouches.

Tuesday November 27-30, 1982

Abbey and I took a 4-day road trip up the coast headed north to the Redwood National Park near Crescent City. On the way Abbey asked me to pull over outside Point Arena, a tiny coastal community with a spectacular coastline used in movie sets. He took my hand and led me down a steep hillside covered in purple bougainvillea to a hidden pristine white sandy cove. We made love in our leather jackets while listening to the crashing waves. We talked about gentle Helmut, how he lives all alone. We wished him well. We spent the night in the 1920s Benbow Inn outside of Garberville, a favorite hideaway of Spencer Tracy and Katherine Hepburn. Straight lovers, gay lovers. It's really all the same.

The highpoint was the redwoods, the tallest trees on earth. We had the place to ourselves. The silence was occasionally broken by deep sustained chords, like those from a massive cathedral organ, as the towering giants swayed ever so slightly in the breeze. Off in the distance we heard giant muffled thuds, coming from the snow-covered ground, as if dinosaurs were playing a game of tag. Looking up to the sky, Abbey detected massive clumps of packed snow, high up near the top, sliding across the sunlit branches slick with wet needles, falling free to the forest floor with mighty thumps.

WEDNESDAY DECEMBER 1, 1982

By the time we were ready to head to the airport back to the Big Apple, we'd fallen in love with San Francisco. As I hugged Jim and then Philip, a strange chill came over me. I recalled that disturbing article published a year and a half ago in mid-1981 in the New York Native. We had all read it in horror. It was about a very rare form of cancer that had struck some gay men in New York and San Francisco. It was always fatal. The initial warning bells were met with anger and denial. I thought of all those hundreds of gay men we'd been enchanted with in the past week. Their beautiful relaxed smiles, their coy playful eyes. Were they safe? Were Jim and Philip safe? Were Abbey and I safe? I hugged them all again.

THURSDAY DECEMBER 2, 1982

It's been two weeks since we had group therapy. I really missed seeing everyone. We're overdue. Tonight is my session # 25.

Brandon and Stanley must have nerves of steel. They are really being tested by the adoption system. Gays get the crumbs left over on the bottom; the babies no straight couple would ever adopt. Often the mothers are overwhelmed single moms, ill equipped and over stressed. Some are drug addicts. Their babies will require extra medical attention, and oceans of love if they are to adjust to their new lives. Brandon and Stanley are up to the challenge. Now it's just a long waiting game.

Graham had hoped he and Jed could have a relationship. But Jed was totally straight with Graham about Max. That option is closed. Graham has been hanging out in Julius' again. A least he has a few friends there.

Eric and Aaron are opening up their own graphic design firm with a lesbian couple. They all met in grad school at Yale. They hope to corner the New York City gay graphics market. Their name will be Q Graphics. Eric sounded all excited. Terrence congratulated he and Aaron and wished them great success.

Darko reported Jerry's individual therapy sessions with Terrence are fine, but the process has barely started. Darko showed great patience. Meanwhile, he's already decorated his Christmas tree. He invited everyone to join he and Jerry in their over-the-top Christmas party on December 15th.

Steve reported that he and Gordon joined a gay men's book club. It meets weekly at member's homes. Steve has an old leather buddy named Douglas who is a member. Steve and Gordon figure this will help introduce them to new gay men who are interested in something other than sex. Sounds cool. Afterwards, on the side, I asked Steve if his friend Douglas was my friend Douglas from the Bennett Building. Bingo! He is.

I reported that Abbey and my interview with the guys who own the house on Beach Hill went extremely well. We really liked both of them. Sounds like we'll fit in nicely. The floor plan looks very interesting. We signed on for a full share in the master bedroom. Season opens April 1st.

Terrence announced a new single gay man will be joining the group next week. His name is Franklin. He's 40, Black, owns his own local business, the Christopher Street Bookstore. The group gasped, that's the sex shop with the backroom.

My goodness! How could I forget to mention Helmut? Terrence asked everybody to sit down again. "Abbey has something he needs to share with us." I told them everything, detail by detail. There was dead silence. When I finally finished Terrence asked the obvious question. "When it was all over, what was the sum of your encounter? What were you left with Miles, looking back on it now, twelve days later?" I am left with love. Especially love for Helmut, the wiser experienced older man. He treated Abbey and me with total respect and the deepest love gay men can share. Helmut was a gentle lover, a wise teacher, a protective older brother and the missing father we never had.

"Thank you for sharing, Miles."

FRIDAY DECEMBER 3, 1982

Tonight after work Abbey is meeting me at the Metropolitan Museum of Art to see the unveiling of their Neapolitan Baroque Creche, a twenty-foot-tall blue spruce Christmas tree surrounded by terracotta figures. It's thick branches hold dozens of life-like angels in silk robes. At its base is a crowded nativity scene with the sacred family and all the usual characters, assorted animals, herdsmen and kings. It is a tradition I look forward to ever year. At home, Jim and I never had more than a puny miniature Norfolk pine for Christmas. Like Charlie Brown's. Pathetic. The Met's Neapolitan Christmas tree is always the one I love the most.

SATURDAY DECEMBER 4, 1982

Our friend Matt from the Pines Co-ops recommended it—the Healing Center on 14th Street. Matt's a cool, super nice guy. Once a week they have a hands-on event in the evening to promote spiritual, mental and physical well-being. Matt is a regular. He invited us to join him. It's for both straights and gays. They dim the lights low; everybody gets comfortable and takes off their shoes and belts and lies down on pillows on the carpeted floor. It starts off with chanting, burning sage, ringing bells and meditation. You are invited to place your hands on the person next to you. They can be a total stranger. It's not supposed to be sexual, although it is of course. You might choose to touch a spot like the shoulders or neck or forehead or feet, places where we often hold onto tension. I was lying down next to Matt. He placed a hand square on my crotch. It went hard. He took a long squeeze and then retreated for the rest of the evening. It went on for over an hour. It was very relaxing, except for Matt's long squeeze. That was a turn-on. Abbey and I made a few new friends, urban hippie types. It was definitely a lot of fun. Something different.

SUNDAY DECEMBER 5, 1982

Abbey and I were feeling more than a little horny. We hadn't fooled around since Jim and Philip took us to the San Francisco Eagle with its notorious backroom in the Castro a week ago. I suggested the Stud. Abbey preferred the Ramrod because they keep the lights on. Very good point. That way we can actually have a conversation. We dressed the part, a little raunchy, a little leather. Inside we had a ball. Partnered up with a German couple into oral sex, Dieter and Wolfgang. Fine with me. What cock and what cocksmen. Afterwards, we talked in broken English for hours on the outside deck. They are here through the holidays. We invited them to our New Year's Party. Super nice guys. We'll have future friends to stay with in Berlin.

MONDAY DECEMBER 6, 1982

I woke up with a precise mental picture of Wolfgang's German cock, hard as stone, like a Bernini sculpture. I lovingly recalled each curve and fold. I instinctively snuggled tight into Abbey's warm backside, my hand all over his soft butt cheeks. Abbey took hold of my boner, which by now had somehow become Wolfgang's and Dieter's as well. The four of us were completely lost in an erotic sex orgy, our real and imagined boundaries indistinguishable.

Tuesday December 7, 1982

I reviewed the construction bids with Robert for his new P-town house. Four bids in total, we went with the second highest, my preferred contractor Glenn. Glenn is a perfectionist like me and Robert. We are in good hands, thank God. I congratulated Robert. Construction will start in early January as the weather permits. Everything looks good. Robert was absolutely thrilled. He thanked me profusely. Abbey and I are invited to Robert's Christmas party next Monday after work.

Wednesday December 8, 1982

Tonight they lit the tree at Rockefeller Center. I always go. For me it's the official start of Christmas. Abbey and I stopped in at the tiny Teuscher Chocolate shop facing the long pool. I just wanted an excuse to see Jose at the counter. He's just the sweetest kid on earth. Long before I met Abbey, Jose and I used to fool around in the tiny backroom with the front door locked. Jose gives great head. Ah, those days are over; but what wonderful memories. God bless him. I wished Jose a Merry Christmas with a warm hug. He always lets me feel his soft bubble butt for a minute. He knows I mean no harm.

Thursday December 9, 1982

Group Therapy session #26 with Terrence and the boys.

Terrence introduced the new guy, Franklin. He's 40, Black and owns and manages the Christopher Street Bookstore. The group was speechless. We all recognized him from the shop. It's a major adult gay sex shop with sex toys and porno videos. Plus, it has one of the hottest backrooms in the West Village. The basement "grotto" is a free-for-all sex club. On rainy days the place is packed. Franklin must recognize all of us by sight. Franklin is a good friend. I've been in the store dozens of times buying all kinds of things related to sex, from lube to cock rings to tit clamps. And the backroom has fond memories. It's where I had my first sex with a real leatherman named Dick. God, was he hot! Guys from all over the world go there to cruise.

First thing we all noticed was the most obvious—Franklin wasn't in his full leather drag like he always wears in the store. He was wearing beige chinos with a red Izod sport shirt. He's very handsome. Trim, athletic, sexy with gorgeous black skin and white teeth like Sidney Poitier. Movie star material. We were all a little intimidated. What was he doing in our group therapy?

Terrence opened the discussion. "So Franklin, what do you want to get from group therapy?" Franklin stood up. He was direct. He'd obviously given the whole subject a lot of careful thought. "I need help. All day long, day after day, I'm surrounded by hot horny guys looking for kinky sex toys, hot leather accessories or the latest triple-X videos. I watch an endless stream of gorgeous and not so gorgeous guys into the backroom or the sex club in the basement. I watch them leave, sometimes together as couples, but usually alone. Some look euphoric, others look crushed. When I finally close up shop at 2 am and turn on the lights it's always the same. Used poppers and condoms, pools of cum everywhere. It's all good business. I'm not complaining. I'm human too. I buy plenty of these items myself. I've even enjoyed plenty of anonymous sex with guys in the backroom. But it takes a toll on me long-term, on my relationship, my personal life. You see, I'm a romantic, in love with the sweetest guy in the world, Anthony, a home body, the love of my life. It's next to impossible to join together the two halves of my life. I need help. Franklin sat down, looking exhausted. Terrence thanked Franklin for being so open. He told everyone that it would probably be best if we all thought about what Franklin said, and next week we can all share our thoughts. Did that sound reasonable? Everyone agreed, great, so we held that topic until next week.

Meanwhile, poor Brandon went next. He and Stanley thought they had an adopted child, a tiny baby girl. They got the phone call at 9:00 pm and rushed to the airport, flew out to Cleveland on an overnight flight, taxied directly to the hospital and after waiting three hours were informed by a nurse that the birth mother wanted to keep her baby girl after all. End of story.

Graham has met a new boyfriend at work. His name is Freddy. He's in the insurance division of the firm. He's ten years older than Graham, 42 versus 32, British, with an adorable accent. They met over coffee in the firm's employee lounge. Sexy in an understated British way. The topic of English musicals somehow came up and that was it. They both know the words and melodies to every English musical written over the last 50 years. That may be a slight exaggeration, but just barely. Graham looked great. Terrence wished the new couple all the best.

Eric and Aaron are extremely busy setting up Q Graphics in their new space in a ground floor loft on Broom Street in Soho. Eric landed their first client, a large gay-owned dental practice that wants a total makeover. He was very excited.

Darko and Jerry are feeling closer than ever. Jerry has stopped his tearoom visits. In his one-on-one therapy with Terrence they did a lot of role-playing. Jerry discovered that tearooms were just an extension of his fear of intimacy. With Terrence's help, Jerry is opening up to Darko for the first time in his life. Darko started to cry. We had a group hug.

Steve reported that he and Gordon love the new gay men's book club. Our mutual friend Douglas made them welcome. Actually, the session happened to be held at Douglas' loft in the Bennett Building. There are ten guys. They're reading Marcel Proust's Remembrance of Things Past. Steve said Douglas was the intellectual heavy-weight of the group. Terrence asked Steve to elaborate. "Douglas is amazing. He has a brilliant mind that connects opposites. Plus he's very loving. He never speaks down to anyone." "Good luck Steve and Gordon. Have fun!

I told the group about our exciting encounter at the Ramrod on Sunday with the two Germans, Dieter and Wolfgang. Great oral sex. I had a ball. Terrence asked me if Abbey and I will continue exploring sex in threesomes and foursomes? He also reminded me of our late-night sex adventure under the Brooklyn Bridge with Helmut and his leather buddies a few weeks back. "That adventure feels more like a dream, like when you had sex with the gondolier or the priest in Venice. Months ago you talked about resuming a monogamous lifestyle once you found Mr. Right. That was well before Abbey arrived. Whatever happened to that plan?" I was quite embarrassed. Terrence was right. I had told him precisely that. I never followed through. I answered as best I could.

"When I first met Abbey we were completely monogamous for a few months. As Abbey opened up, I discovered he was much more experienced sexually than I was. I admired that. While I was locked up with Jim for almost a decade, Abbey was busy connecting to others in the gay bars and baths, at GAA and New York Gay Switchboard. I was impressed. I was flattered to be at his side. Abbey was my guide to the unknown, the leather bars, the baths, the backrooms. But Abbey took it slow. First we were just voyeurs. Then I started having sex on the side—a sweaty jogger in a tearoom, a leatherman in the Ramble at lunch, or a horny salesman in a dressing cubical. I'd always tell Abbey all about my new adventures; he never judged me; he listened. He knew I was searching for my new identity. Then we started pursuing hot sex encounters together, like a team. We went back to the Ramble together to find Helmut, to sample the goods together, to get to know him as a gay man. We did the same with Douglas and Angelo, with Daniel and Patrick. We'd talk about these shared adventures for hours. What worked, what didn't. These were not faceless encounters. We always exposed our hearts, looking for a balance, making a connection to these men. Abbey and I have no regrets; it was always beautiful."

Terrence eventually spoke after a long pause. "Miles, you've been on a long journey. You've changed trains numerous times. Your journey is not over. I feel you have not found your new center completely. It's a work in progress. It's much more complex than the one you formed with Jim. It has tentacles. This new one pulls others into its orbit. You still have a lot to do, you must rest, stop and reflect, then you and Abbey may decide together to push out again, explore new ground, or maybe not. That is your choice to make with Abbey in due time. But I sense it's already quite clear."

Friday December 10, 1982

Tonight was Hanukkah. Abbey and I celebrated Shabbat dinner at Shirley's. Angie and Patrick joined us. Shirley adores both of them. Patrick has been attending Torah Studies at Shirley's temple. Angie is off to India after New Year's. She recently received a Fulbright scholarship to study architecture in India for a year. Shirley lit her menorah candles and recited the traditional blessing over the wine and bread. We all played Scrabble together. Shirley always wins.

Saturday December 11, 1982

Abbey and I decided to brave the shopping crowds and walk up Fifth Avenue from the Village taking in the Christmas window displays. B. Altman's, Macy's, Saks, Bonwit Teller, and Tiffany are among my favorites. Macy's and Saks always have the best windows for animated displays. In Brooks Brothers they were serving eggnog. The sidewalks were mobbed. Forget about the ice-skating rink at Rockefeller Center. It was packed. We poked briefly into St. Patrick's to see the decorations. Out front a boys' choir from Connecticut was singing Christmas carols. By the time we walked back to the loft we were starved. Even Chinatown was decorated for Christmas. Szechuan dinner was perfect.

Sunday December 12, 1982

We can't take Midtown any longer. We decided to avoid the shopping crowds and stay below 14th Street all day. Still, there were long lines out the door at Matt McGhee's Christmas tree ornament shop on Waverly Place. Matt always makes me think of Ebenezer Scrooge. He always has this unbelievable scowl on his face, as if he hates Christmas. I'm thankful Abbey is Jewish and isn't into Christmas. With Jim we always decorated a tiny Norfolk pine. One box of twelve small ornaments. Took all of ten minutes tops. Not like my Catholic childhood where Christmas decorating went on for weeks.

Christopher Street was busy with plenty of sexy Santa's walking around, many wearing soft Santa caps and red bandanas in their rear pockets. We ran into Jack and Wolf outside Jack's building at One Christopher Street. They looked terrific. We're invited to their Christmas party next Saturday. Wouldn't miss that one for the world.

I needed a break from all this Christmas crap. I asked Abbey, "How about a little cock?" "Sure Miles, I can arrange that." He took us to the Hellfire Club, always busy on a lazy Sunday afternoon. Perfect. Inside a dozen guys were going at it full tilt to disco music. I particularly enjoyed Mr. and Mrs. Claus, a tall drag queen being butt fucked against a column by the butchest Santa I've ever seen. The two of them were really putting on a show. At one point she yells out loudly, "Get out the big one Santa. You can do better than that!"

MONDAY DECEMBER 13, 1982

Christmas was only twelve days off. Tonight was our first Christmas party of the season at Robert's condo in the Village. The party was pure Robert. Everything was white including the hundreds of white Christmas lights stretched high up across the ceiling like an enormous white spider web. Robert himself was dressed in white Levi's and a pressed white CK tee. Even the caterers were all in white carrying white trays of French champaign. A cellist in the entry hall was playing Bach softly. Robert handed me a Christmas present with a warm hug. A small white box to be opened later. The living room was packed wall-to-wall, mostly with attractive gay men in denim and leather and a few exotic female creatures to add some color. Brandon and Stanley were there in tuxedos. The biggest surprise was Terrence and Thomas. I had no idea that Robert was in private therapy with Terrence for the last several years. I'm sure they must have discussed me plenty. Oh well, small world.

Back home in the loft I opened Robert's Christmas present, the classic white-on-white Georg Jensen wristwatch with a black leather band. I'd always wanted one. Robert had the back of the watch engraved. "For Dearest Miles, My Only Architect, love Robert."

Tuesday December 14, 1982

Matt called up and invited Abbey and me back to the Healing Center tonight. Sure, I loved it last time. A good escape. I was on my own since Abbey promised Shirley he'd install a new DVD player in her bedroom. Tonight's session was being held in somebody's loft in Tribeca. I arrived a little early. Matt asked me if I wanted to smoke a joint on the back fire escape before they got started. Sounded like a good idea. Then I saw it coming. I remembered Matt's hand on my cock last time. Sure enough, once Matt had me on the fire escape, his hand was inside my jeans squeezing my dick. Now what? I really like Matt, so I couldn't say no. He's just a sweet hippie. He proceeded to give me the best blowjob I'd had in weeks. It was a perfect 10, unbelievable. He was really into it. We were out there in the dark for half an hour, making love on the fire escape, like in that Laura Nyro song Up on the Roof.

Wednesday December 15, 1982

Darko and Jerry's Christmas party on Henry Street in Brooklyn Heights was a trip. They are both seriously into Christmas decorations. Walking through the door was like entering one of those overcrowded Christmas stores packed solid with burning yule logs, tree ornaments, miniature nativity scenes and hundreds of angels. It felt claustrophobic. The punch was too strong. Actually, everything was too strong. Abbey and I snuck out after thirty minutes.

On the sidewalk we ran into Billy and Jeremy. They live just a block away also on Henry Street. They met Darko and Jerry recently on the promenade and were invited to their Christmas party tonight.

Billy pulled me aside. He and Jeremy want to get together soon for a foursome. "Sounds great! How about New Year's Eve at our loft, if you're free. It would be a great way to welcome in the New Year. By the way, tell Jeremy I really have the hots for his shiny bald head. It's driving me crazy. I just want to lick it clean."

Thursday December 16, 1982

It was nice having a break from Christmas. Tonight was group session #27.

The new Black guy Franklin started off. I actually know Franklin pretty well through his sex shop. I like him. He's a real character. Gorgeous black skin. A serious body builder. He asked the group if they had any advice for him. He was open to discuss anything. Graham asked if he'd ever considered hiring a store manager to run the store and the sex club so he didn't have to go there every day. Franklin said he'd tried that two years ago for a month, but he really missed the nightly excitement. Every night holds a new mix of guys that he enjoys interacting with.

I smiled and welcomed Franklin into our group. Then I said it sounded like he wants it both ways—the exciting sex scene and the quiet domestic bliss at home with Anthony. I told him I'd been through both this past year myself and had discovered it's hard to maintain both. It seems to me it's pretty much either one or the other. "It sounds like Anthony wants you to pretend the sex scene that goes on daily in your shop is not a part of life for either of you. But, of course, you know it is, at least for you it is, right? I don't mean to tell you how to live your life Franklin. I just want you and Anthony to be happy." Franklin gave me a warm hug.

Terrence jumped in. "Please tell us more about Anthony. How did you meet?" His reply surprised a few guys. "I met Anthony two years ago in the 'grotto.' That's the basement sex club at the store. Anthony was getting screwed by a Black buddy of mine named Wolf. They were really going at it. I stopped to watch. 'Hey Franklin, try this hot kid out, he only likes Black dick. He's nice and tight.' Well Wolf was right on the mark. I was hooked from the first butt-fuck. From that moment on Anthony was my butt-boy. I adore him. He's incredible. Our sex is off the chart. He moved in within days. Late every night, after I close up, I wake up Anthony asleep in our bed and we make love. Anthony is a good Catholic boy. He was even an altar boy. He never misses Sunday Mass at St. Patrick's. Anthony's really a home body. But he has a secret. He craves Black dick up the ass. I know how to satisfy him. He knows what I like. So that's our story. It's not complicated.

218

But my life is split into two parts, the angel and the devil. I'm going a little crazy." Terrence replied, "Look Franklin, I hear you but, let's call a spade a spade. You are wrapped up in the gay sex industry; you own and manage a popular sex club; your shop sells it all. A lot of guys would kill for the job. Anthony, your angel, is your business. That's fine, no problem, he really sounds like a sweet guy. Your relationship sounds beautiful. But you need to realize that with your shop you're providing an important service to the gay community, an outlet for gay men to explore their sexuality in a safe space. We're not devils, just guys looking for a release, some fun, if we're lucky maybe some love. For many of your clients, your store is it, the center of their most intimate contacts with other men. I've been there myself plenty, looking for love. Frankly, it could be better, more supportive of us guys who go there. There's not any mention of safe sex that I've seen. That's not right. You could do better. By taking a little better care of your clients, showing them more care, love and respect, you might discover you feel better about your own life." I had never heard Terrence so upset. Franklin had touched a raw nerve. The group gave Terrence a standing ovation.

Eric jumped in. He was very excited. "Yeah, you could make it more attractive. It's so dark. Put up some hot safe sex info, show videos of hot guys having safe sex, dispense free condoms, maybe put in a few skylights to let the sun in. Give out free bottled water. Sell hot t-shirts up front next to the dildos! Make the front room more of a social space for guys to meet. Be creative."

Franklin looked a bit surprised, even stunned. He thanked the group and said we'd given him an awful lot to think about. I wondered if we'd ever see him in group again.

Brandon announced that he and Stanley are taking a break from the adoption search until after Christmas. I don't blame them. It's just too much. They don't know what color to paint the new baby's room until they know if it's a boy or a girl. They don't have a strong preference, either will do. Any race is fine, black, white, yellow or brown. They just want the waiting to end, so they can start living again as a family.

Graham and Freddy are planning a trip to London sometime after New Year's. They want to see English musicals, the more, the better. Graham asked me if Cambridge was worth a day trip? What a question. That's like asking, is it worth waiting on line to see the Mona Lisa?

Eric was shaken up. Over the weekend someone threw a cinderblock through the front plate-glass window of Q Graphics. No one was hurt, but Eric felt like he was the victim of a hate crime. The fact that it happened in Soho on Broom Street in the middle of the day, only made it hurt more.

Darko said Jerry is feeling like a new person. He hasn't been to the tearooms in weeks. He's decided to volunteer on the phones at New York Gay Switchboard. It was Terrence's suggestion. I must tell Abbey. He'll want to talk to Jerry. Give him a few pointers.

Steve said he was feeling ashamed. He admires what the other guys in group are doing to help others. He feels selfish. The new book club is great, but he and Gordon are looking for something more rewarding, more involved with helping people. Terrence suggested Steve and Gordon volunteer together, it might bring them closer together. There are numerous groups in the Village that help troubled gay teens. "The Hetrick Martin Institute is excellent. Convenient for you in Astor Place. Maybe that would be a good fit for you guys. You both have a lot to offer."

I was moved by Steve's confession. I gave him a warm hug. He broke down in my arms. I told the group I shared all of Steve's concerns, we are not that different, he is my brother. I told him I want to discuss all this with Abbey and see what he thinks we might do.

Friday December 17, 1982

Chuck and John always give a big Christmas party in John's family brownstone on Gansevoort Street. Marley's ghost might well live within those old walls. The house and Christmas are synonymous. Lots of holiday decorating, real gingerbread cookies hanging on the tree, candles instead of electric lights, plus Chuck is a great cook. Chuck always invites his whole office, including a few unbridled screaming brats, and John always finds at least half a dozen aspiring writers in town looking for a free meal. There's an octogenarian Aunt upstairs who adds a bit of gravitas. And then there are Chuck's string of tricks and assorted hangers-on. That can yield at least a good dozen or two more. Many have empty dance cards for the evening, a few come with a mouthwatering bulge in their crotch. John's cat Walter, named after the poet Whitman, set his tail on fire as he tip-toed past the pair of candlesticks in the kitchen window. Fortunately, Abbey came to the rescue. The smell of burning fur was most unpleasant.

SATURDAY DECEMBER 18, 1982

Abbey and I were invited to Jack and Wolf's Christmas party. Wow! Jack rented the Gagosian Gallery in Soho for the evening. The rock star gay caterer Chloe really stole the evening. His pumped-up athletic waiters were dressed in Chloe's signature plain black leather vests over bare chiseled chests. But below that, Jack gave Chloe very specific instructions. Instead of the usual black leather hot pants, the waiters were to wear BIKE jock straps, that's right, in assorted colors, their beautiful butts on public display for an easy pat or a nice long squeeze. The guests were almost entirely leathermen, decked out in their most elaborate black leather outfits. I spotted Douglas and Helmut, Billy and Jeremy, Steve and Gordon, Jed and Max. Simon was solo. The hosts were also in leather, but their huge red and white Santa hats stood out as the only touch of color in the entire gallery, save for the huge oversize Andy Warhol portraits adorning the walls.

SUNDAY DECEMBER 19, 1982

I have a Christmas tradition with Angie. Dinner at the Four Seasons at the base of the Seagram Building during the week of Christmas. Since Abbey and I will be in London, we are a bit early this year. I invited Bob and Dave to join us. Bob, like me, knows it's New York City's best restaurant, hands down. The Mies van der Rohe / Philip Johnson dining hall is stupendous, the separate bar room is equally grand. An enormous Picasso wall tapestry adorns the glass fronted hall that joins the two chambers. It feels more like a major art museum than a Midtown high-priced restaurant. Giant slabs of African rosewood paneling. Shimmering draped beaded curtains temper the view out to the city. The signature four trees, one for each season, illuminate the corners of the large square central pool. If I were a waiter, this is where I'd work. Grand, elegant, austere, breathtaking. The meal stretched out for three hours. Some say the food is so-so. Why complain, you are in heaven dummy.

MONDAY DECEMBER 20, 1982

Abbey and I had a long talk about Steve and Gordon's dilemma. We're really in the same boat. We mostly just look after ourselves. Abbey used to be active at GAA and New York Gay Switchboard helping people in real trouble. He misses all that. I value my volunteer work at GMHC. Abbey suggested we invite Steve and Gordon over for dinner and discuss the possibility of doing volunteer work at The Hetrick Martin Institute, perhaps we could start something there together. It sounded like a great plan. I called Steve. He loved the idea. We're on for dinner tomorrow night. That settled, we decided it was a good time to go for a walk through the Financial District. The Greek temple façade of the New York Stock Exchange was adorned with six huge evergreen wreaths with enormous red bows, each hung from a tall Corinthian marble column.

TUESDAY DECEMBER 21, 1982

Michael was in his very best mood—charming, funny, generous and loving. It was the day of the afternoon Arch Plus Christmas party, the first in our gorgeous new offices on Hudson Street. The three partners, Michael, Paul and me were wearing traditional red and white Santa hats. The trays of catered food were spread out on the black ash conference table. Michael had organized a Canadian game of gift swapping—good gifts, gag gifts—something from his childhood long past. It was ripe with off-color humor. Michael was his usual brilliant showman. Anne, our sweet prim-and-proper English receptionist, was the perfect foil for Michael's indelicate vulgarity. At the climax Michael fell to the floor in a spasm feigning an epileptic fit. He really should have been a Vaudeville comedian.

By the end, I felt a little wasted and was really looking forward to our dinner discussion with Steve and Gordon. I made my carbonara pasta. We brainstormed about what we could offer HMI. Steve proposed safe sex classes. It would be fun, lots of humor and at the same time it would meet a serious need with gay teenagers. Lots of play-acting. With two couples we could even cover the topic of safe gay sex in three and foursomes. Great idea. Sounds cool. I suggested we propose it to the guys in charge at HMI after Abbey and I return from our trip to London for Christmas. All agreed. We had a group hug.

WEDNESDAY DECEMBER 22, 1982

Abbey and I are off to London for a week. It's great to see Abbey so excited. I'm falling in love with him all over again. This is his first trip to Europe. I want to spoil him silly. The hotel John has recommended in Bloomsbury is perfect, that is, it's inexpensive but comfortable. Repton House. We soon nicknamed it Reptile House, after some of the lodgers we'd encounter around the breakfast table each morning. It was a converted town house, one of several dozen identical brick facades with white marble stoops in a straight long row filling the entire block. It was always a challenge finding the right front door. At the corner was Russell Square, a lovely London park in front of the huge Victorian brick pile of the Hotel Russell. By the second day we had figured out that breakfasts there were far superior with warm scones, clotted cream, Stilton cheese, stewed prunes and hot oatmeal.

THURSDAY DECEMBER 23, 1982

John took us for lunch at an Indian hole-in-the-wall restaurant near the Thames, cheap but outstanding, locals only. He tried to play a joke on us by secretly ordering the lamb vindaloo, pretending it was another mild dish, to get a cheap laugh at our expense. But it wasn't that spicy. The joke was on John. Afterwards, he drove us around the city in his little sports car. Just sitting in the passenger's seat while traveling in the left lane was disconcerting, especially around corners. I couldn't possibly drive there. In the afternoon John took us to Greenwich to see the world-famous Prime Meridian Line.

Friday December 24, 1982

On the afternoon of Christmas Eve we were invited by Shirley's cantor Bruce to attend a choral rehearsal of the Boys Choir in Westminster's Abbey. Like being at a private concert. Bruce was in London working on his PhD. What a treat. The music was cerebral. We were seated in the same steeply raked carved choir seats that the boys were using. The boys were all extremely adorable, as you can imagine. I wished our friend Trevor, the geriatric psychiatrist, was here. He's really into this kind of thing. The only problem was the one-thousand-year-old stone building was totally unheated. The damp cold went right through everything, just like when I was in Venice. No wonder all the English have rosy red cheeks.

Saturday December 25, 1982

Christmas Day, Joseph invited us to his new loft in Knightsbridge, for an elaborate sit-down dinner for twelve. Joseph was another of Abbey's glamourous boyfriends from the past, this one a famous A-list choreographer that Abbey met at the Ramrod. They had a month-long fling while Joseph was in New York working at the Met on an edgy new production of Verdi's Macbeth with Sir Peter Hall. We attended the opening night performance, a fairly shocking event for poor Joseph. An angry audience erupted with extended booing in Act I as the witches crisscrossed the proscenium on broom sticks flying through the air. A bit too reminiscent of Margaret Hamilton in The Wizard of Oz. This would mark Joseph's last assignment at the Met.

Sunday December 26, 1982

Boxing Day was a whirlwind of sightseeing, starting at the National Gallery in the early morning, drooling over their gorgeous Chardin still lifes. Now, this guy knew how to paint! In the afternoon we popped into Westaway & Westaway across from the British Museum to pick up an English wool blanket for the bed back home. Night Watch. The Sir John Soane's Museum in Lincoln's Inn Fields was a special treat. The great architect's home was full of antiquities, architectural models, furniture and paintings—any gay man's dream. We decided to skip high tea at the Savoy and instead check out the sauna at the Sweatbox. Plenty of British knob to sample. The Brit fags are all so polite with their charming English accents. "Cheerio lads! At your service!" After all that street sleaze, we opted for an elegant Indian dinner and theatre in Covent Garden.

MONDAY DECEMBER 27, 1982

We needed a little break. Abbey spotted it on a movie marquee. Once Upon a Time in America, Sergio Leone's latest masterpiece about Jewish gangsters on the Lower East Side in the 30s. Our kind of movie. Themes of childhood friendships, love, lust, greed, betrayal and loss. Sounds like my life story, you think? It runs for three and a half hours. Between the gangster scenes there is an amazing take where the actress Tuesday Weld confronts a lineup of half a dozen horny male gang members. She's looking for the guy who got away, the one who butt-fucked her during a chaotic bank robbery. The men unzip their flies and pull out the goods to assist with her search. She goes down the lineup, one by one, carefully holding and squeezing each with saucy comments like. "Very nice, I'd like to get to know you." "Charmed, charmed." and "I think we may have already met."

WEDNESDAY DECEMBER 28-29, 1982

We easily slept on the flight home. Our overhead luggage included six place settings of classic Wedgewood White China. Angie would approve. We picked them up at half price in Crate & Barrel. Finally back home in bed, as I gave Abbey his nightly back rub, he told me he had a major announcement. On the plane ride home he decided it was time to take the plunge. Next week he will enroll at Hunter College to get his Bachelor's. He'll continue working part-time at the Asian importers. Shirley and I had already offered to split the tuition. It will probably take four years, but he's extremely excited. The momentous news somehow ended up giving me a raging hardon. After passionate love making, Abbey drifted off to sleep in my arms.

THURSDAY DECEMBER 30, 1982

It's been two weeks since my last group therapy. Session #28. We took a break over Christmas. A lot has happened since then. I'm particularly

225

looking forward to seeing Franklin. I hope he's alright. We were pretty hard on him last time.

We started with a long group hug. It felt good to be back with the guys and Terrence. Franklin never showed up. Everyone felt his absence.

Brandon was glowing. Finally, the adoption came thru. It's a darling little Black girl. They are naming her Jamie Irene after Stanley's mother. Brandon and Stanley got the call from Lander, Wyoming at 2:30 am on Monday. They flew into Riverton via Denver on a small private plane since the Riverton runway is tiny. Then they drove several hours in the dark to Lander. The sun was rising as they checked into the local hospital which was new but surprisingly small. They were getting a lot of scrutiny from the nurses and staff. This sort of thing has never happened before in Lander. Finally, after an hour an administrator came out to formally check them in. Thankfully, a black male nurse aid was there to make Brandon and Stanley feel welcome. This guy had to be gay. What a swish. Most of the other staff just stared in disbelief. Brandon and Stanley took it all in stride. Nothing could diminish their joy as they held their new baby daughter in their arms for the first time. Many in the group started to cry as they gave Brandon a standing ovation. Terrence gave Brandon a bear hug.

Graham reported that Freddy wants to live with him full time. He doesn't care whose apartment or if Graham wants to find another, that's fine too. He just wants to come home to Graham every night. It's very touching after all Graham has been through lately. Freddy is already planning a trip to England around Valentine's Day. He wants Graham to meet his parents who are in their 80s and still live in a charming cottage in the Cotswolds. The plan is to do a week in London seeing musicals and a week in the English countryside just relaxing. Plus a side trip to Cambridge.

Eric reported that all's well at Q Graphics. His lesbian partner Juanita landed the job to do all the graphics for the new LGBTQ Community Center on 13th Street. It's the perfect client to give Q Graphics the visibility they're looking for. If this trend continues, they may have to find a bigger office space. Eric also told the group that Terry and Bob from their red-hot foursome in the Pines last October called to arrange yet another orgy at their apartment. Both he and Aaron are totally onboard with the idea.

Darko reported that Jerry had a tearoom relapse. It turns out that at the extreme north end of the Brooklyn Height's Promenade is a pair of old public toilets. Darko always thought they had been locked up permanently by the City Parks Department. Not so. Jerry was out alone on an afternoon walk on the Promenade when he noticed a hot kid walk inside the men's room. After waiting several minutes with a no show, Jerry ventured inside, his heart racing. The kid had his trousers down at a urinal. He turned to show off his hardon. They had sensational oral sex. The kid took down Jerry's phone number. Jerry is conflicted. He wants to stop, but when the opportunity presents itself, he always gives in. Terrence told Darko not to lose hope. Like any addiction, tearoom sex can't just be turned off like a light switch. It takes time.

Steve was all excited. He explained that he and Gordon were approached by Abbey and me to volunteer together offering safe sex classes at the Hetrick Martin Institute that Terrence had recommended. The volunteers coordinator Tony was a really cool Black guy who they really connected with. He had a similar back story to theirs. He used to spend all his free time fucking around in backrooms. When a trick told him about HMI, he discovered a whole new world. Tony loved the idea of play-acting and safe sex classes and suggested they might look into their program called Sexplanations, a safe space for teens to discuss questions about sex and relationships. It's really fun. The group leader is stepping down. Tony thought Steve, Gordon, Abbey and I would be perfect with all our real-life experience and our fun sense of humor. Great! Who knows, maybe we could eventually take over.

I shared the good news that Abbey is signing up at Hunter next semester. That got a standing ovation with cheers. Terrence asked me what Abbey wants to study. "Definitely psychology, maybe sociology, maybe he'll do a double major. He should study whatever he loves."

Lastly, Terrence announced that Franklin called him this morning to thank him and the entire group for their suggestions. He and Anthony have started talking for the first time in their relationship. Franklin told Terrence it was both very scary and wonderful. He's ashamed of how he behaved with the group. He said he was a pompous ass. He asked for everyone's forgiveness. Terrence thanked him and wished him all the best in the New Year. I felt badly, as if I'd pushed Franklin out of the group unfairly. An awkward silence fell over us.

When at last we heard a knock on the door, we all breathed a bit easier. As the door opened slowly, I saw a pale blond young man. He was wearing white painter's overalls over a pink t-shirt. Being mostly white, I immediately thought of an angel, like one of those Neapolitan Christmas angels Abbey and I had seen at the Met. But this angel was not terribly angelic, he was too sexy, too adorable, too beautifully queer. Right behind the youth was Franklin, smiling, tall and radiant. I immediately walked over to welcome them in. I teared up. Franklin handed me a white cake on a silver tray. The whole group stood up to give them a standing ovation complete with whistles and hollers. Terrence welcomed young Anthony. I hugged dear Franklin. I was crying. Franklin held me like a father. It turned into another beautiful holiday party, this one for our family.

FRIDAY DECEMBER 31, 1982

Finally, it's New Year's Eve, but more importantly, tonight is the special party I helped arrange for Billy and Jeremy with Abbey and me in my loft, starting on the early side. I checked with everyone and got a green light to also invite the German leather couple Dieter and Wolfgang who Abbey and I met at the Ramrod a month ago. They live in Berlin and are vacationing in New York City over the holidays. Super nice guys. So that makes six guys total. I hope it goes well for everybody. These things are always a bit of a gamble. But if it clicks, just think, what a wonderful way to bring in the New Year.

It's not so much an 80s orgy as a 60s love-in, complete with flower children. I asked everyone to skip the leather and think bell bottoms and tie dye. I still had the stuff in the back of my closet. I even had an extra Village People outfit for Jeremy. It was super cool when we opened the door to find Billy looking more like a laidback Donovan than a Spike leatherman. Of course, Abbey had the real stuff from the six months when he lived in San Francisco, dating a groovy hippie from the Jefferson Airplane. He had the look down perfectly in sandals, sexy bell bottoms, a tie-dye sunburst tee and a very suggestive crotch pose that invited "free love." I made Alice B. Toklas's hash brownies. The two Germans came as twins wrapped in old tattered American flags out of Easy Rider with inviting plump pink jock straps. Music was strictly of the period: Strawberry Fields Forever, Hurdy Gurdy Man, Aquarius, A Piece of My Heart, Macho Man, Knights in White Satin, A Whiter Shade of Pale and House of the Rising Sun. It somehow turned into a totally oral event. Forget the sling. Rather, it was a cock fest with plenty of holiday dick to go around for everyone. The leather sofa got a workout as we stripped and got down and dirty. It was a 60s love-in in the best sense—no egos, but creative, complete sharing as an organic whole—always exchanging roles, trading off, evolving, reinventing itself. We made love together, to each other, to our six beautiful cocks. It was perfect.

Afterwards, we grabbed heavy blankets and went up to the roof to take in the fresh night air, the city lights, the twin towers. Fireworks at midnight. Goodbye 1982, Hello 1983.

Parting company in the wee hours was surprisingly emotional. Billy and Jeremy lingered behind, unwilling to part so soon. We made gentle love one more time, Billy and me, Abbey and Jeremy; then trading off for another pairing, and again one more after that. It all felt so natural. Bonds of love holding us all together—safe and strong.

SATURDAY JANUARY 1, 1983

It's New Year's Day.

My 1982 Diary is full. That's about all you can really say. It's not as if

I finished a marathon and got a gold ribbon. Yes, today is a new year, but everything else feels pretty old, pretty much the same. Although the party last night was something really special which I'll cherish forever. The perfect farewell to a tumultuous year, 1982. I still have my new beloved Abbey, my oldest friend Jim, my girlfriend Angie, my hot sex buddies Bob, Simon, Douglas and especially Helmut. I'm blessed with my new friends Jack and Wolf, Billy and Jeremy. And a brand-new baby girl, Jamie Irene. I may take another painting class with Daniel. I'm really looking forward to our adventure at The Hetrick Martin Institute with Steve and Gordon and the kids. I'm not ready to leave Patrick behind and I'll never part from Terrence. Besides, I love Terrence. How could I leave him? I'm thinking about a month road trip to Italy with Abbey next fall. We'll fall in love all over again. I'm still working through my sex-on-the-brain issues. That will probably never change. But that's alright. I'm happy.

We got an envelope in the mail from our new landlord Eddie. He's bought an old SRO hotel near Macy's at Herald Square and plans a gut renovation. Wants to move us artists out of the Bennett Building. New space to my design, a rent stabilized lease, and a spectacular view of the Empire State Building. I told Abbey we better check it out on Saturday morning. I feel a new adventure coming.

CAST

OF

CHARACTERS

Wolf, New York University grad student, Miles's Black sex buddy

Andrei, surgeon-in-training, Miles's Saint hookup

Angie, architect, Miles's straight girlfriend

Douglas, high-brow art editor, Miles's upstairs' sex buddy

Franklin, Black sex shop owner; Miles's good friend

Robert, toy designer, Miles's almost sugar daddy

SPRING

Richard, architect, Miles's Cornell classmate

Michael, architect, Miles's ex-boss and new sex buddy

Daniel, Miles's New York University painting instructor

Simon, architect, SOM co-worker, gay leatherman

Jack, older Mine Shaft regular, Miles's last call

Timmy, New York University student poet, Wolf's roommate, tearoom addict

Stanley, architect, Miles's SOM boss

Lawrence, Miles's trick from Man's Country

Mark, architect, Miles's older straight brother

Chrisy, New York University academic, Mark's girlfriend

Jose, Miles's trick from St. Mark's Place

Chuck, Miles's oldest friend from Cornell

John, Chuck's lover

Franco, Italian banker, Miles's Tuesday afternoons' sex buddy

Tony, Italian gym bod, Miles's steam room buddy

Tyrell, architect, SOM Senior Partner

Jed, gay biker, Miles's one-night-stand sex buddy

Damian, GMHC Buddy Program Director

Patrick, AIDS patient, Miles's new GMHC buddy

Sean, AIDS patient, Billy's new GMHC buddy

Max, Jed's sugar daddy, Miles's new old man

Abbey, Asian Import Coordinator, Miles's new beloved

Shirley, New York City temple administrator, Abbey's Mom

Susie, writer, Abbey's middle sister

Janet, anthropologist, Abbey's older sister

Donald, Abbey's first ex-lover

Joel, Abbey's last ex-lover

Steve, New York University economics PhD grad student, Miles's 1st therapy crush

Graham, CPA, Miles's 2nd therapy mate

Brandon, children's book editor, Miles's 3rd therapy mate

Darko, tearoom addict, Miles's 4th therapy mate

Eric, graphic designer, Miles's 5th therapy mate

Judy, architect, Abbey's favorite cousin

SUMMER

Fred and Steve, Abbey's buddies, S&M couple

Michael, restaurant owner, Miles's tearoom pest

Mel and Dan, Miles's twin sister and brother-in -law

Tex, gay hustler from Man's Country, Miles's trick

Jeremy, Billy's new beloved

John, British architect, Arch Plus co-worker

Michael, Miles's business partner, Arch Plus

Virginia, co-worker Arch Plus, sour puss

Anne, British Arch Plus receptionist

FALL

Angelo, NYU exchange student, painter, Miles's sex buddy

Jimmy, Abbey's straight boyhood buddy

Philip, CPA, Jim's new SF boyfriend

Marsha, Michael's girlfriend, Goldman Sacks analyst

Tim, Miles's trick from Man's Country

Matt, regular, Hands-On Healing Center

Jose, boy toy, Teuscher Chocolates

Anthony, home body, Franklin's beloved

Matt, shop owner, Christmas ornaments, Dickensian ghost

WINTER

Joseph, British choreographer, Christmas Day dinner host

Tony, Program Director, HMI, safe sex workshops

Jamie Irene, Brandon and Stanley's newly adopted baby girl

Dieter and Wolfgang, German party mates, New Year's Eve

Eddie, Miles and Abbey's new landlord in Midtown Manhattan

Abbey, psychology student, Hunter College, cum laude

Miles, queer architect who finally finds true love in New York City

www.ingramcontent.com/pod-product-compliance
Lightning Source LLC
Chambersburg PA
CBHW010113270326
41927CB00018B/3370